MY BIG BOOK OF
READING
AND SUMS

Written by Colin Clark
Illustrated by Stephen Holmes

Brown Watson
ENGLAND

Contents

MESSAGE TO PARENTS

This book has been designed to help children in the 5-9 age range to learn and practise their early English language and maths skills. The facts are presented simply and clearly with the use of amusing, colourful illustrations, simple text and numerous games and puzzles. In this way, the book can be used in the home to complement and reinforce the educational process that takes place at school.

The answers to all the exercises and puzzles can be found at the end of each section.

ISBN : 0-7097-1380-0
This edition first published 2000 by Brown Watson
Reprinted 2001
The old Mill, 76 Fleckney Road,
Kibworth Beauchamp,
Leicestershire LE8 OHG, England

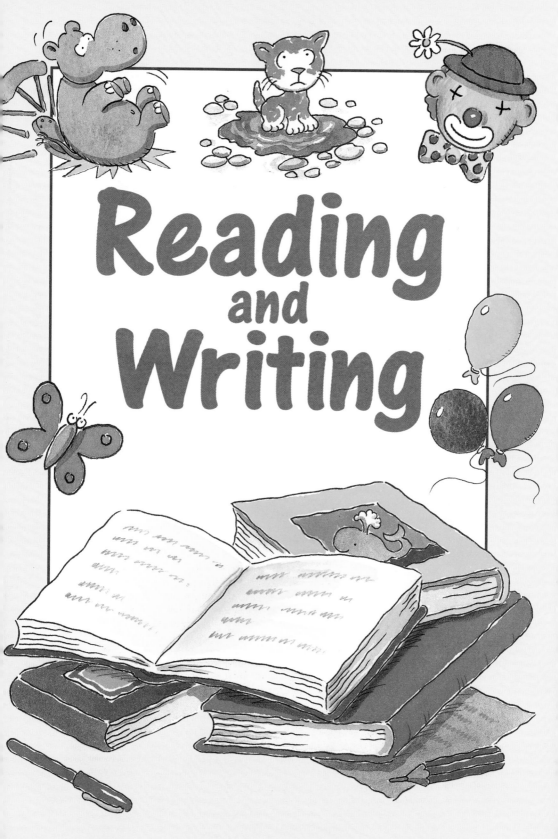

Reading and Writing

MEET THE JONES FAMILY

This is Jack Jones.
Jack is eight years old.

This is Jenny Jones.
Jenny is six years old.

Jenny and Jack live in this house.

They live with their mother, Mrs. Jones, their father, Mr. Jones, and their granny, Granny Jones.

The Jones's house is also home to Sniff, the cat, Smelly, the dog and Speedy, the tortoise.

How many people and how many pets are in your home?
Write down all their names on your work pad.
Try and write a sentence to describe each pet.
For example: 'I have a brown dog called Chocolate.'

THE JONES'S HOUSE

There are four bedrooms in the house.
Mr. and Mrs. Jones have a bedroom. It is tidy.

Granny has a bedroom. It is tidy.

Jenny and Jack share a bedroom. It is always in a mess.

The other bedroom is a spare room just now. When Jenny is a little older, she will move out of the bedroom she shares with Jack and move into the spare room. Then Jenny and Jack will each have their own bedrooms and there will be two bedrooms in a mess.

How many bedrooms are there in your house? Write down the names of the people in each bedroom on your work pad.
Write a sentence to describe each bedroom.
For example: 'My little sister's bedroom wall is covered with pictures of pop singers.'

MR. JONES, THE HANDYMAN

Mr. Jones is a hard-working handyman. He is always busy. He does all kinds of work around the house and in the garden.

He paints the inside and outside of houses.

He makes wooden book-shelves and cupboards.

He replaces broken roof tiles.

He builds stone walls.

8

Are you good at working with your hands?
List the things you can do on your work pad.

Here are four pictures of Mr. Jones at work.

1)

2)

3)

4)

Write a sentence describing what
Mr. Jones is doing in each picture.

MRS. JONES, THE LADY WITH THE TIME TO LISTEN

Mrs. Jones is also a busy person. While her husband is out at work, she works at home. She makes breakfast for the family, then takes the children to school. She makes sure everyone has good food to eat, clean clothes to wear and a clean house to live in. She also has her own computer which she uses to earn money to pay for everything that is needed.

Mrs. Jones works so hard that she often falls asleep in front of the television in the evening. But she is the first one up in the morning and she always has time to listen to anyone who needs to talk to her.

Read the text below. Are the following sentences about Mrs. Jones true or false?

1) The first thing Mrs. Jones does in the morning is take the children to school.
2) Mrs. Jones goes out each day to an office to work on a computer.
3) Mrs. Jones does the cooking and cleaning.
4) Mrs. Jones watches TV in bed in the evening.
5) Mrs. Jones always has time to listen to you.

Is your mum as busy as Mrs. Jones? Write a description of your mum's busy day on your work pad. Show it to your mum and ask her if she thinks your description is accurate.

JACK, JENNY'S BIG BROTHER

Eight-year-old Jack Jones is interested in lots of different things. His favourite subjects at school are English and computer studies. He loves football and wants to be the goalkeeper in the school team when he is older. He is a keen swimmer, particularly good at the butterfly stroke. He likes climbing and often pretends he is a mountaineer. He enjoys his piano lessons and would like to be a famous pianist when he grows up. He often has to look after Jenny, his little sister, but he doesn't mind because they are very good friends.

Answer the following questions on your work pad.

1) What would Jack like to be in the school football team?

2) When Jack goes swimming, which is his favourite stroke?

3) When he is climbing, who does Jack pretend to be?

4) What does Jack want to be when he grows up?

Have you ever been to a musical concert or have you seen one on TV? Write two or three sentences about the music you like or an instrument you play.

JENNY, JACK'S LITTLE SISTER

Jenny is two years younger than Jack. She also likes school, especially English and stories. On Monday mornings, the teacher tells the class a story which she either reads from a book or makes up herself. She then asks the class if anyone would like to tell a story of their own. Jenny loves doing this and has told some wonderful ones. For example, the day she spent as a princess, the time she appeared on television and the occasion when Granny fell off her motorbike!

Jenny's stories would be much better if only she used a greater variety of 'describing words'. Jenny uses the adjective 'nice' far too often. For example, here are a few sentences from her stories. Rewrite them, replacing 'nice' with another adjective from the list below.

1) Nice Jack dived into the water to rescue the nice dog.
2) The nice girl with nice hair was wearing a nice dress.
3) The nice cat ran after the nice mouse.
4) The nice witch turned the nice prince into a frog.
5) The nice sun caused the nice tree to throw a nice shadow.

beautiful	normal	brave	fair	pretty
drowning	lazy	ugly	tabby	bright
handsome	tall	little	flowing	long

GRANNY ON HER MOTORBIKE

Granny Jones is not like other grannies. Other grannies enjoy knitting, shopping, watching TV and drinking cups of tea. Jack and Jenny's granny is very different. She loves to put on her helmet and leather biking suit and ride off into the countryside on her motorbike.

The motorbike used to belong to Grandpa Jones and he and Granny would often go out on it. After Grandpa died, Granny kept the bike for herself. Jack and Jenny can't wait until they are old enough to be allowed to go out with their motorbiking granny!

If you have to tell someone how to get somewhere, you give them directions. For example, you might say: 'Go out of the house and turn left. At the end of the street, turn right. Go to the grocery store, then turn left again...' and so on.

Below is a street map of the town in which the Jones family lives. Granny has to deliver a parcel to a friend's house. Give her clear directions so that she does not take the parcel to the wrong house. Write the directions on your work pad.

Draw a map of the area around your house. Mark the names of the streets, local shops and anything else which might help a friend to find their way.

SNIFF, THE CAT

Sniff is a tabby cat who lives with the Jones family. The children found her one rainy day sitting sadly in a puddle. They brought her home and looked after her. Now Sniff is a large, contented cat. When the weather is good, she likes to stay out all night. If it is cold or wet, Sniff prefers to sleep indoors in her own basket. Sniff likes to settle on people's laps. If they do not move about too much, she begins to purr very loudly. If they do not sit still, Sniff jumps down with a hiss and walks away with her tail swishing.

Sniff hunts the birds in the garden and would love to catch them - but she's too slow! Every time she leaps out of the bushes, the birds fly away and leave Sniff looking mean and disappointed.

Read the story of Sniff carefully, then answer the following questions on your work pad. Please write complete sentences.

1) Where did the children find Sniff?
2) When it rains, where does Sniff sleep?
3) If the person whose lap she is on does not move about, what does Sniff do?
4) What noise does Sniff make when she is angry?
5) Where does Sniff hide when she is hunting birds?

SMELLY, THE DOG

Smelly is a large dog with long, droopy ears whose favourite pastime is chewing bones. When Mrs. Jones gives him a fresh bone, he runs and settles down and chews it for hours on end. Just when the Jones family think he's chewed it to death, Smelly usually sneaks away and buries it. Days, or even weeks later, the bone reappears. It's smelly (that's why he got his name) and horrible, but he chews it again for hours before finally putting it aside for ever.

Sometimes, the bone has been buried in the Jones's garden. However, when they find out the bone is buried in a neighbour's garden, the Jones family have a lot of explaining and apologising to do. Smelly doesn't understand what all the fuss is about.

Smelly has buried his bone somewhere in the Jones's garden. The clues below will help you to find it. Write down on your work pad exactly where the bone is.

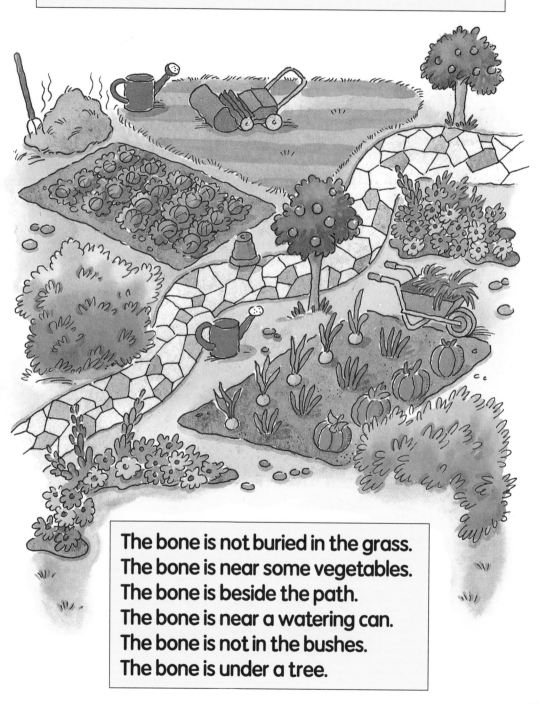

The bone is not buried in the grass.
The bone is near some vegetables.
The bone is beside the path.
The bone is near a watering can.
The bone is not in the bushes.
The bone is under a tree.

SPEEDY, THE TORTOISE

The Jones's third pet is a tortoise, called Speedy. He moves around very slowly, eats slowly as well, and particularly enjoys lettuce, cucumber slices and banana. In the summer, Speedy lives in the garden, which is safe because he can't get out of it. He creeps around and spends a lot of time sleeping under bushes. Speedy spends the winter sleeping in a straw-filled hutch in the garage. If he was left out in the cold, he would fall asleep and never wake up. In the warmth of the garage, he wakes up every year when the spring comes.

The sentences opposite tell us about Speedy's busy day. The story does not make sense because the sentences are not in the right order. Rewrite the sentences in the correct order.

Then it was time for another rest, so he plodded back to the bushes. He plodded as fast as he could to the food dish. At daybreak, Speedy woke up. There he found a breakfast of lettuce leaves and banana slices waiting for him. He had had a busy day! In the afternoon, he did it all again. He came out from under the bushes, where he had spent the night. After that, Speedy plodded back to the bushes for a good night's sleep. He walked back to the food dish for his supper.

ANSWERS TO THE TESTS

Page 9 - MR. JONES, THE HANDYMAN

1) Mr. Jones is making a kennel for the dog.
2) Mr. Jones is putting in a new pane of glass.
3) Mr. Jones is repairing the wheel of the pram.
4) Mr. Jones is hanging a picture.

Page 11 - MRS. JONES

1) False
3) True
5) True

2) False
4) False

Page 13 - JACK, JENNY'S BIG BROTHER

1) the goalkeeper
3) a mountaineer

2) butterfly
4) a pianist

Page 15 - JENNY, JACK'S LITTLE SISTER

1) Brave Jack dived into the water to rescue the drowning dog.
2) The beautiful girl with fair hair was wearing a pretty dress.
3) The tabby cat ran after the little mouse.
4) The ugly witch turned the handsome prince into a frog.
5) The bright sun caused the tall tree to throw a long shadow.

Page 19 - SNIFF, THE CAT

1) The children found Sniff in a puddle.
2) When it rains, Sniff sleeps in her basket.
3) She begins to purr very loudly.
4) When Sniff is angry she makes a hissing noise.
5) Sniff hides in the bushes.

Page 21 - SMELLY, THE DOG

Smelly has buried his bone right in the middle of the picture, at the side of the path, under the tree.

Page 22-23 - SPEEDY, THE TORTOISE

At daybreak, Speedy woke up. He came out from under the bushes, where he had spent the night. He plodded as fast as he could to the food dish. There he found a breakfast of lettuce leaves and banana slices waiting for him. Then it was time for another rest, so he plodded back to the bushes. In the afternoon, he did it all again. He walked back to the food dish for his supper. After that, Speedy plodded back to the bushes for a good night's sleep. He had had a busy day!

Spelling

THE ALPHABET

Name each of the following objects pictured below. Each one begins with a different letter of the alphabet. To help you, we have put in the first letter of each word in alphabetical order. We have also put in a dash for each missing letter. Write the words on your work pad.

1) a _ _

2) b _ _

3) c _ _

4) d _ _

5) e _ _

6) f _ _ _

7) g _ _ _

8) h _ _

9) i _ _

10) j _ _

11) k _ _

12) l _ _ _

13) m _ _ _ _

14) n _ _ _

15) o _ _

16) p _ _

17) q _ _ _ _ _

18) r _ _ _

19) s _ _ _ _ _

20) t _ _ _

21) u _ _ _ _ _ _ _ _

22) v _ _ _ _ _

23) w _ _ _ _ _

24) x _ _ _ _ _ _ _ _

25) y _ _ _ _

26) z _ _ _ _

WORDS BEGINNING WITH d

There are 10 things in the picture below which begin with the letter **d**. Can you find them all? Write the answers on your work pad.

ANIMAL NAMES ENDING WITH **t**

There are 10 animals shown below with names ending with the letter **t**. Can you spot them? Write the answers on your work pad.

MAKE YOUR OWN WORDS

The following letters of the alphabet are known as consonants:

b c d f g h j k l m n
p q r s t v w x y z

Words often begin with two of these consonants put together in a 'blend'. We have listed some of these blends below. Choose a blend to complete each of the words pictured and write the completed words on your work pad.

st cl dr gr pl tr sc

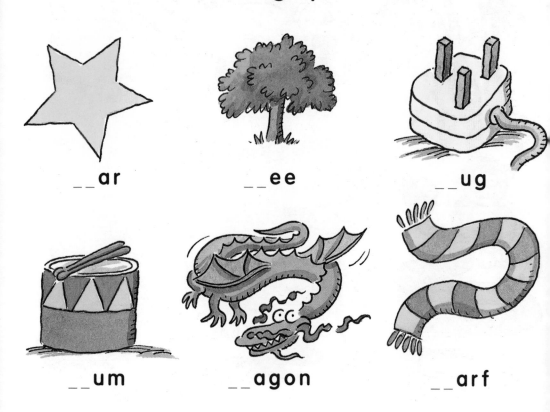

__ ar

__ ee

__ ug

__ um

__ agon

__ arf

32

__ eps

__ ass

__ ock

__ ant

__ oud

__ ain

__ apes

__ ip

__ ones

__ iff

__ ales

__ unk

__ ay

__ um

__ amp

THE DIFFERENCE AN **e** MAKES

At the end of many words, when an **e** is added or taken away, we get a new word that sounds quite different to the original one.

Try adding an **e** to the words printed on this page to make new words that go with the pictures. Say both the old words and the new ones and write them down side by side on your work pad.

can

pip

fir

kit

man

not

pan

win

bar

Now take away the **e** at the end of the words on this page and write the new words on your work pad.

care

mate

tape

huge

fine

tripe

dame

plane

scare

plume

cape

hate

LOOKS THE SAME, SOUNDS DIFFERENT

These letters of the alphabet are known as vowels:

a   e   i   o   u

Lots of words contain two vowels side by side, but sometimes the same two vowels together can make more than one sound.

ea has two sounds: as in st**eal** and inst**ead**.

Write the words **steal** and **instead** on your work pad. Then, under **steal**, list the words pictured below which sound like **steal** when you say them. Write down under **instead**, all the words which sound like this when you say them.

br _ _ d   h _ _ d   t _ _

st _ _ m   p _ _ ch   thr _ _ d

Sometimes, when a vowel and a consonant are in combination, we also find that they look the same but have different sounds.

ow has two sounds: as in s**low** and n**ow**.

Write the words **slow** and **now** on your work pad. Then, under **slow**, list the words pictured here which sound like **slow** when you say them. Write down under **now**, all the words which sound like this word when you say them.

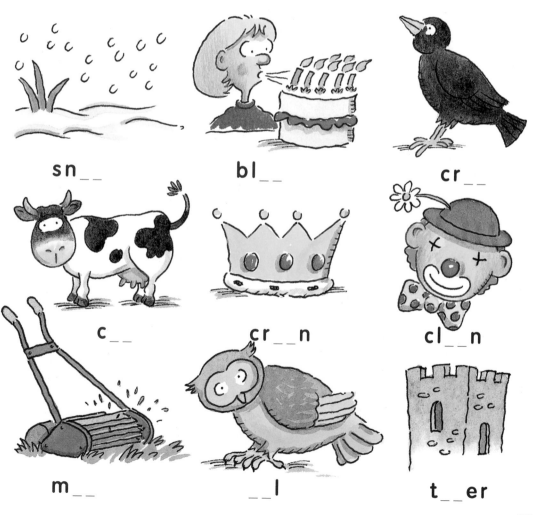

s n _ _

b l _ _

c r _ _

c _ _

c r _ _ n

c l _ _ n

m _ _

_ _ l

t _ _ er

LOOKS DIFFERENT, SOUNDS THE SAME

Sometimes letter combinations look different but sound exactly the same when we say them.

oy and **oi** make the same sound: as in b**oy** and b**oi**l.

Write the words **boy** and **boil** on your work pad. List underneath them all the words pictured below which have the combination **oy** or **oi** in them.

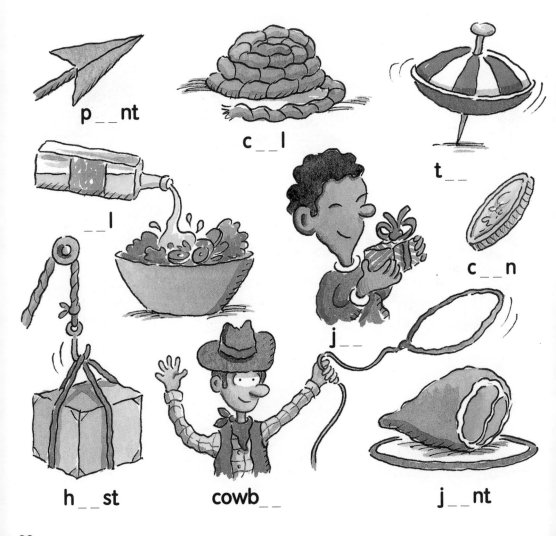

p _ _ nt

c _ _ l

t _ _

_ _ l

c _ _ n

j _ _

h _ _ st

cowb _ _

j _ _ nt

ay and **ai** make the same sound: as in **pay** and **paint**.

Write the words **pay** and **paint** on your word pad and list underneath them all the words pictured below which have the combination **ay** or **ai** in them.

r _ _ n

displ _ _

p _ _ nter

r _ _

pr _ _

s _ _ l

sn _ _ l

compl _ _ n

tr _ _ n

39

WORDS IN TWO PARTS

Some words are made up of two shorter words joined together.

Here is an example.

key + hole = keyhole

There are four picture sums like this shown below. Each sum shows pictures of two small words that together make up a longer, two-part word. Write down the answer to each picture sum on your work pad.

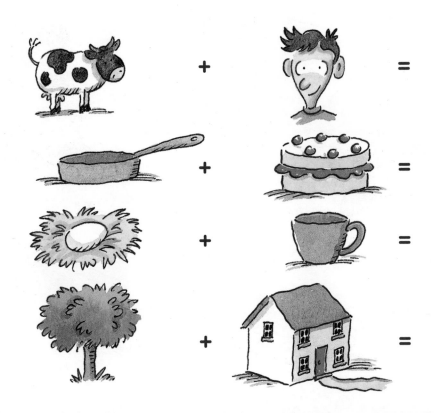

ANIMAL WORD SQUARE

The names of 13 different animals are hidden in
this word square. Find their names and write them
on your work pad. We have pictured some of the
animals around the square. Take care! Not all the
animals pictured are in the word square!

w	p	a	r	r	o	t	q	l	z
f	a	h	e	d	n	i	m	i	o
s	n	a	k	e	r	g	e	o	t
a	d	r	o	a	b	e	w	n	y
h	a	m	s	t	e	r	o	c	t
d	r	o	u	r	m	e	p	i	g
h	t	n	p	i	x	w	a	r	e
o	s	k	a	n	g	o	o	s	e
r	y	e	z	k	o	s	r	f	t
s	h	y	o	n	a	t	o	w	l
e	m	i	b	a	t	e	t	b	u

Pages 28-29 THE ALPHABET

1) ant
2) boy
3) cat
4) dog
5) egg
6) fire
7) girl
8) hat
9) ice
10) jar
11) key
12) leaf
13) mouse
14) nest
15) oar
16) pig
17) quilt
18) rose
19) smoke
20) tree
21) umbrella
22) violin
23) watch
24) xylophone
25) yacht
26) zebra

Page 30 - WORDS BEGINNING WITH **d**

duck, doll, dinosaur, door, dartboard, darts, drum, desk, dog, drawing

Page 31 - ANIMAL NAMES ENDING WITH **t**

bat, parrot, rabbit, cat, rat, goat, newt, elephant, ant, piglet

Page 32-33 - MAKE YOUR OWN WORDS

star, tree, plug,
drum, dragon, scarf
steps, grass, clock,
plant, cloud, grain,
grapes, drip, scones,
cliff, scales, trunk,
tray, plum, stamp

Pages 34-35 - THE DIFFERENCE AN **e** MAKES

cane, pipe, fire,
kite, mane, note,
pane, wine, bare

car, mat, tap,
hug, fin, trip
dam, plan, scar,
plum, cap, hat

Page 36 - LOOKS THE SAME, SOUNDS DIFFERENT

instead
bread, head, thread
steal
tea, steam, peach

43

Page 37

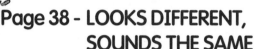

slow
snow, blow, crow, mow
now
cow, crown, clown, owl, tower

Page 38 - LOOKS DIFFERENT, SOUNDS THE SAME

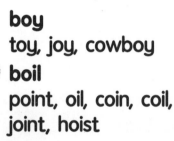

boy
toy, joy, cowboy
boil
point, oil, coin, coil, joint, hoist

Page 39

pay
ray, pray, display
paint
rain, snail, train, complain, sail, painter

Page 40 - WORDS IN TWO PARTS

cowboy, pancake, eggcup, treehouse

Page 41 - ANIMAL WORD SQUARE

parrot, panda, snake, tiger, lion, hamster, pig, monkey, goose, horse, bat, goat, owl

Punctuation

WHY DO WE HAVE PUNCTUATION?

Here are the first few lines of the famous story by Lewis Carroll, Alice in Wonderland. They have been printed without any punctuation. See if you can make any sense of them.

Alice was beginning to get very tired of sitting by her sister on the bank and of having nothing to do once or twice she had peeped into the book her sister was reading but it had no pictures or conversations in it and what is the use of a book thought Alice without pictures or conversation

It is not easy to read this, is it?

Now try reading it again with punctuation.

Alice was beginning to get very tired of sitting by her sister, and of having nothing to do: once or twice she had peeped into the book her sister was reading, but it had no pictures or conversations in it, "and what is the use of a book," thought Alice, "without pictures or conversation?"

It is easier to read with punctuation, isn't it?

WHAT DO PUNCTUATION MARKS MEAN?

There are eleven punctuation marks that we use in written English. These are:-

full stop	•	The bells are ringing.
question mark	?	Why are the bells ringing?
exclamation mark	!	What a noise the bells make!
comma	,	The bells are ringing, because there is a wedding.
hyphen	—	The bell-ringers are tired.

dash	—	The bells are ringing – but the old dog does not hear them.
brackets	( )	The bells (all four of them) are ringing.
colon	:	All four bell-ringers are ready: Mr. and Mrs. Brown and the twins.
semi-colon	;	There is something wrong; one of the bells is cracked.
inverted commas	" "	"I hate the bells," says Granny.
apostrophe	'	The bells are so loud; it's not Granny's fault she hates them.

FULL STOP

Just as every sentence must begin with a capital letter, so a full stop is the usual punctuation mark which shows that a sentence has ended. It is the punctuation mark that we use most often at the end of sentences.

The following words do not make sense unless we put a full stop at the end of each sentence.

My name is Katie I am seven years old I live in the country my Mum and Dad have a farm

My name is Katie. I am seven years old. I live in the country. My Mum and Dad have a farm.

Write the following words on your work pad. Then, divide them into sentences by putting in the full stops. Do not forget to begin each sentence with a capital letter.

You should see the mess in my bedroom the cat climbed in the window while I was out now my bed is covered in mud

In the following sentences, the full stops are in the wrong places. Write the sentences with the full stops where they ought to be. Don't forget the capital letters!

Jill had to do something. To save her dog the witch had almost dragged Scruffy. Out of the house Jill picked up the soup spoon and gave the witch a crack. On the knuckles the witch screamed and let go of Scruffy.

QUESTION MARK

At the end of a sentence that asks a question, we put in a question mark. When we are talking, the way we say something tells the other person we are asking a question. When we are writing, we must put in the question mark.

Copy these sentences on to your pad and put a full stop or a question mark at the end of each one.

Where is my biscuit

Someone has eaten your biscuit

Who has eaten it

Did the dog eat it

It looks like it

Look at the picture above. Write down the answers to the questions on your work pad.

1) How many mice can you see?

2) What is one of the mice eating?

3) Where are the other mice hiding?

4) What are the other mice looking at?

5) What is the old mouse holding?

EXCLAMATION MARK

An exclamation mark can be used instead of a full stop at the end of a sentence. It can also be used even after just a word or two, to express emotion. For example:

Look at that!
The horse has eaten my hat.

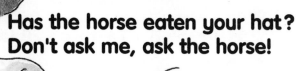

Has the horse eaten your hat?
Don't ask me, ask the horse!

Help! The horse has eaten my hat.

Write the following on your work pad. Put either an exclamation mark or a question mark at the end of each one.

What is it   **What a face**   **Ouch**

Disgraceful   **Does it hurt**   **Splash**

COMMA

Very often, to make the sense clearer, it is necessary to have a brief pause, or a number of brief pauses, in a sentence. The most common punctuation mark used for these brief pauses is the comma.

For example, it is much easier to read and understand the sentence on the right than the one on the left.

To get to the pet shop turn left then second right then go straight on to the next corner where you will see it.

To get to the pet shop, turn left, then second right, then go straight on to the next corner, where you will see it.

We also put a comma after names in a list, instead of using the word **and** all the time. The second sentence sounds better, doesn't it?

Hilary and Hannah and Hilda have put on their best hats because they are going to a party.

Hilary, Hannah and Hilda have put on their best hats, because they are going to a party.

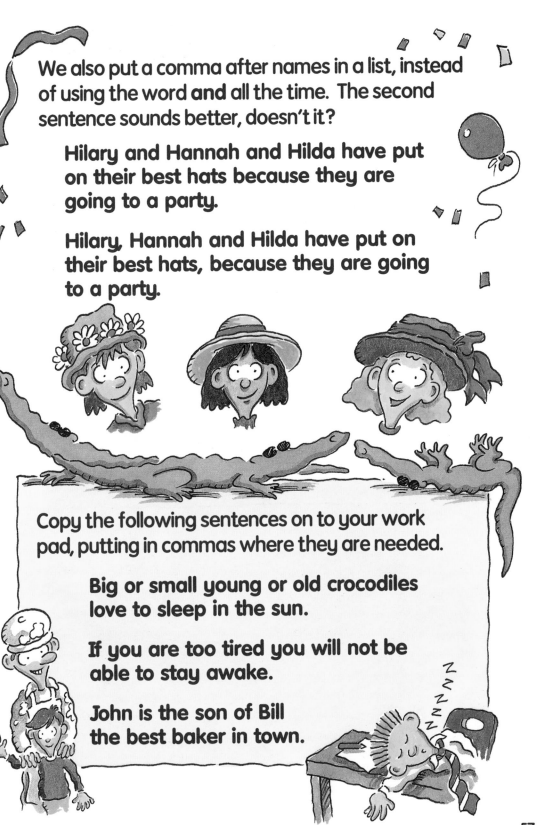

Copy the following sentences on to your work pad, putting in commas where they are needed.

Big or small young or old crocodiles love to sleep in the sun.

If you are too tired you will not be able to stay awake.

John is the son of Bill the best baker in town.

HYPHEN

A hyphen is used to join two words together to become what is called a compound word. For example, the words **well** and **known** are joined together with a hyphen to become **well-known**.

Each of the words in the first line below can be joined with a hyphen to one of the words in the second line to make a compound word. Write all five compound words on your work pad.

twenty	lay	half	right	big
by	term	handed	headed	two

man eating lion   man-eating lion

DASH

A dash is used when a sentence suddenly changes direction.

Dad put on his hat and coat and went out – but he had forgotten to put his trousers on!

Katie's painting of a kite – a very colourful affair – was soon stuck on the wall in her bedroom.

BRACKETS

Brackets can be used instead of dashes before and after a secondary thought in a sentence. Brackets must always be used in pairs. There must be an opening bracket at the beginning and a closing bracket at the end of the secondary thought or extra piece of information.

The children took some books to read (and plenty to eat) on their coach trip to the sea.

The little country mouse gave all that she had (one nut) to the hungry town mouse.

A name in brackets can also make it clear who it is we are referring to in a sentence.

The teacher told John that he (the teacher) had not always done his homework when he was young.

Write the following sentences on your work pad, replacing dashes with brackets where you think it is right to do so.

The girl took off her gloves and her coat – but she kept her hat on.

Fred was a friendly dog – he wanted to lick everyone – but was too big to keep indoors.

Abigail was a beautiful cat – a real Persian – and she was very fussy about her appearance.

COLON

We use a colon immediately before we make a list of some kind or before a quotation.

Aunt Agatha brought everything with her: luggage, handbag, shopping bag, umbrella, cat basket and cat.

Young Percy would often quote Shakespeare: 'Friends, Romans, countrymen, lend me your ears!'

Write the following sentences on your work pad, putting in a colon each time, if you think the sentence needs one.

Morris had three pictures, a pretty mouse, a piece of cheese and the house cat.

The manager addressed the football team, 'On the one hand, you have played with great spirit, on the other, we have lost every game.'

SEMI-COLON

A semi-colon is the punctuation mark for a longer pause than that marked by a comma. A semi-colon is used to join two parts of a long sentence. It is used instead of words like **and, but** and **because.**

Wilf was not allowed to play football that day; he had left one boot at home.

The other animals did not like it when Hattie came to tea; she broke all their chairs.

Write these sentences on your work pad, putting in a semi-colon where one is needed.

Bill and Ben are two gorillas – Bill is bigger.

Sally tripped over the rug and fell on the cat, Sally's dinner fell on Granny.

INVERTED COMMAS

Inverted commas are used to mark the beginning and end of speech. Sometimes there are two inverted commas and sometimes only one.

"How are you, Your Highness?" asked Tom.
"I am very well," replied the princess.
The king said: "I feel terrible."
"I am so sorry, Your Majesty," said Tom.

Remember that all the spoken sentence, including the full stop, question mark or exclamation mark at the end, goes inside the inverted commas.

Sometimes it is necessary to break a spoken sentence into two parts. Then you must always remember to begin and end each part of the sentence with inverted commas. No capital letter is needed at the start of the second half of the sentence.

If the spoken sentence is only reported and the actual words are not used, no inverted commas are required.

"I have a headache," the king told Tom.

The king told Tom that he had a headache.

APOSTROPHE

An apostrophe is used to show that something belongs to someone. The apostrophe is put after the owner and followed by an **s**.

Here is Joe.
Here is a book.
It is Joe's book.

When there are two or more owners, the apostrophe comes after the **s**.

The socks belong to the boys.
They are the boys' socks.

When there are two or more owners and the word does not end in **s** (eg. men, children), the apostrophe is followed by an **s**.

The toys belong to the children.
They are the children's toys.

Some belonging words which end in **s** are called pronouns. They are possessive themselves and do not need an apostrophe.

**his   her   its
ours   yours theirs**

Is that football **yours**?
No, that is the teacher's football.
It is **his**.

The other use of the apostrophe is to show that a letter, or some letters, have been left out of a word.

isn't = is not (the letter **o** has been left out)

I've = I have (the letters **ha** have been left out)

Other examples of words that use the apostrophe are:
    **who's = who is, I'll = I will, can't = cannot
    he's = he is, it's = it is, who'd = who would**

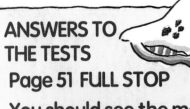

ANSWERS TO THE TESTS

Page 51 FULL STOP

You should see the mess in my bedroom. The cat climbed in the window while I was out. Now my bed is covered in mud.

Jill had to do something to save her dog. The witch had almost dragged Scruffy out of the house. Jill picked up the soup spoon and gave the witch a crack on the knuckles. The witch screamed and let go of Scruffy.

Page 52-53 QUESTION MARK

Where is my biscuit?
Someone has eaten your biscuit.
Who has eaten it?
Did the dog eat it?
It looks like it.

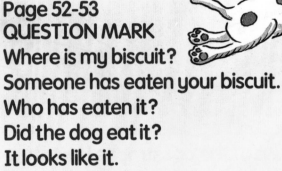

1) Four mice.
2) Some cheese.
3) Behind the loaf of bread.
4) The cat.
5) A walking stick.

Page 55 EXCLAMATION MARK

| What is it? | What a face! | Ouch! |
| Disgraceful! | Does it hurt? | Splash! |

Page 57 COMMA

Big or small, young or old, crocodiles love to sleep in the sun.

If you are too tired, you will not be able to stay awake.

John is the son of Bill, the best baker in town.

Page 58 HYPHEN

twenty-two   lay-by   half-term

right-handed   big-headed

Page 61 BRACKETS

The girl took off her gloves and her coat — but she kept her hat on.

Fred was a friendly dog (he wanted to lick everyone), but was too big to keep indoors.

Abigail was a beautiful cat (a real Persian) and she was very fussy about her appearance.

Page 62 COLON

Morris had three pictures: a pretty mouse, a piece of cheese and the house cat.

The manager addressed the football team: 'On the one hand, you have played with great spirit, on the other, we have lost every game.'

Page 63 SEMI-COLON

Bill and Ben are two gorillas; Bill is bigger.

Sally tripped over the rug and fell on the cat; Sally's dinner fell on Granny.

Grammar

WHAT IS A SENTENCE?

A sentence is usually a group of words which makes sense by itself. A sentence must start with a capital letter and end with either a full stop, a question mark or an exclamation mark. Each of the following is a sentence.

Katie has a dirty face.

Isn't Katie's face dirty?

What a dirty face Katie has!

Sometimes a sentence can be just two words.

Come here!   Go away!   Get washed!

Sort out these mixed up sentences and write them down correctly on your work pad.

on the fence. The elephant is sitting pulling Sally's hair. The monkey is the cake. is eating The mouse

Use the words below to write proper sentences on your work pad. Begin with a capital letter and finish with a full stop, question mark or exclamation mark.

like chocolate do you

out get

much how the apples are

rough sea the today is

VERBS

A verb is the 'doing word' in a sentence — the word that tells us what a person or thing is doing or what is happening to them.

A woodpecker **pecks** on wood.
The truck is **tipping** sand out
of the back.

Pick a verb out of this list to complete each sentence and write the completed sentences on your work pad.

combs   watches
find   carry

Rapunzel _____ her long hair.

It is difficult to _____ all the boxes.

The detective hopes to _____ a clue.

Our cat _____ television all the time.

74

These sentences have the wrong verb in them.
Choose the correct verb and write each sentence
on your work pad.

We pour a lemon.   We squeeze our shoes.

We light a knot.   We tie the fire.

We polish the orange juice.

Pick the correct verb for each sentence and write it
on your work pad.

a) I (cook/clean/paint) my teeth after a meal.
b) The hen has just (cooked/buried/laid) an egg.
c) Please (burn/wash/shake) the plates for me.

THE SUBJECT

The subject of a sentence is the word or words identifying the person, place or thing doing an action. This word can be a noun, a proper noun or a pronoun.

Nouns are the words used for naming things. Names which refer to a person, place or thing individually are called proper nouns and always begin with a capital letter.

Some nouns

for a person – teacher nurse   girl
for a place   – house   kennel palace
for a thing   – egg   pencil torch

Some proper nouns

for a person – Tom   Katie   Queen
for a place   – London France Parliament
for a thing   – Bible   Easter Concorde

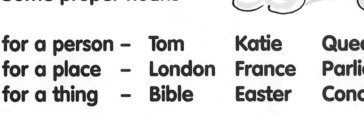

Pronouns are words used instead of nouns. These are the pronouns which we use as subjects:

I   you   he   she   it   we   they

Mary saw Simon pulling faces.
She saw Simon pulling faces.

Mary is the subject of both sentences, but in the second sentence, the pronoun **she** is used instead of Mary.

Can you pick the correct subject for each sentence? Write the sentences on your work pad.

The doctor   Mary   He   The kennel

_____ fell over the football.

_____ was too small for the dog.

_____ put a bandage on Paul's knee.

_____ put on a lovely dress.

THE OBJECT

The object of a sentence is the person, place or thing to which the subject is doing something. The word or words for the object can be a noun, a proper noun or a pronoun.

As in the case of the subject, pronouns are words used instead of nouns. These are the pronouns we use as objects.

me   you   him   her   it   us   them

Ann helped John to wash the dog.
Ann helped him to wash the dog.

John is the object of both sentences, but in the second sentence, the pronoun **him** is used instead of John.

For each of these sentences, write down on your word pad:
a) the subject
b) the object

1) The elephant is wearing a hat.
2) The fairy flapped her wings.
3) Snakes do not have legs.
4) Henry loves ice cream.

Look at the sentences below. Rewrite the second sentence replacing the underlined words with pronouns.

1) Cindy has a new coat. <u>The coat</u> cost <u>Cindy</u> a lot of money.

2) The children had a box of chocolates. <u>The children</u> ate <u>the chocolates</u>.

3) Granny has two cats. <u>Granny</u> lets <u>the cats</u> sleep on her bed.

ADJECTIVES

Adjectives tell us more about nouns. They are 'describing words'.

Here are some nouns. Pick an adjective from those listed below to describe each noun.

1) forest   2) scream   3) game
4) town   5) flower   6) load

yellow   heavy   clever   loud   thick
wooden   quiet   sticky   close   bold

Pick out the adjectives in the following sentences. Write the adjectives on your word pad.

1) Rex is a friendly, little puppy.
2) The shiny aircraft made a roaring noise.
3) The haunted house is in the dark woods.
4) The new teacher had long hair and wore a battered, old hat.
5) Susan had muddy shoes and a torn dress.

Choose the right adjectives from the selection below to complete the following sentences. List your chosen words on your work pad.

1) The _____ cat sat on Mum's hat.
2) _____ sharks try to catch fish in their _____ mouths.
3) _____ Peter had _____ problems with _____ sums.
4) The _____ pot gave off a _____ smell.

ginger   steaming   huge   weeping
difficult   fierce   poor   serious
smiling   truly   best   horrible

Below are ten balloons. Each one has half a word on it. Join the halves together and write the five adjectives on your work pad.

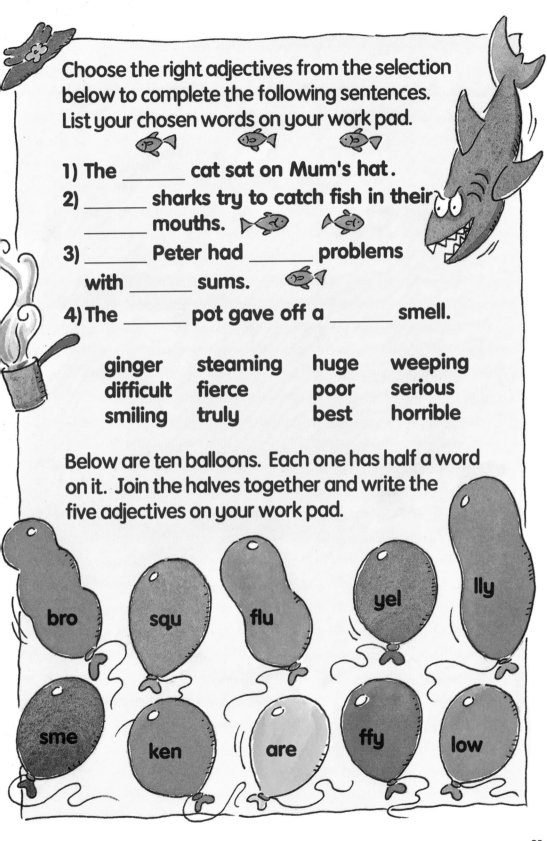

bro   squ   flu   yel   lly

sme   ken   are   ffy   low

ADVERBS

An adverb does for a verb what an adjective does for a noun; an adverb adds more meaning to a verb.

Some adverbs are spelt the same whether they are used as an adjective or as an adverb. For example:

Fred was on the early train. (early as an adjective, describing the train)

Fred's train arrived early. (early as an adverb, adding meaning to the verb **arrived**)

Some adjectives become adverbs simply by adding **ly** to the end of the word. Others have to change spelling to become adverbs.

sweet – sweetly	**poor – poorly**	**rare – rarely**
happy – happily	**gentle – gently**	**speedy – speedily**

Make adverbs from all the adjectives listed here and write the words on your work pad.

regular   **precise**   **wealthy**   **powerful**
heavy   **glad**   **hungry**   **noisy**

Choose the right adverb for each of these sentences. Write them on your work pad.

politely   bravely   beautifully   greedily

1) _____ , he gave up his seat for the old lady.

2) The children _____ went to the cat's rescue.

3) The pigs ate their food _____ .

4) She danced _____ that evening.

PREPOSITIONS

Prepositions are words which are used to tell us where or how someone or something stands in relation to another person or thing. Most prepositions are short words, but some consist of groups of words.

Here are some prepositions:-

under	over	by	near
towards	off	since	upon
through	with	of	on
until	in	at	beside

in spite of   as soon as   because of   except for

Find the preposition in each of these sentences. Write your answers on your work pad.

1) The mouse was sitting beside the cheese.
2) The mouse ran away as soon as the cat appeared.
3) The cat ran along the wall.
4) The dog was tied to the gatepost.

Sometimes, two prepositions are used together.

Bob jumped **down from** the wall.
Bess did not come **until after** we had finished lunch.

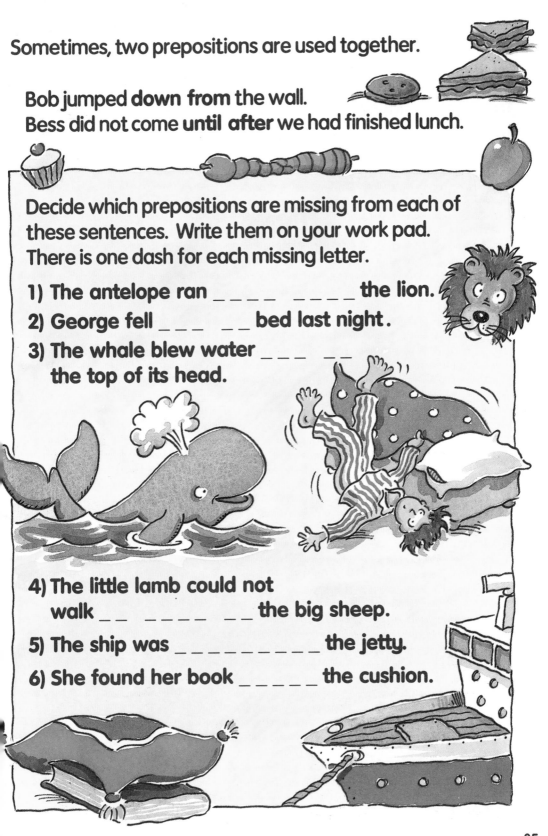

Decide which prepositions are missing from each of these sentences. Write them on your work pad. There is one dash for each missing letter.

1) The antelope ran _ _ _ _   _ _ _ _ the lion.
2) George fell _ _ _   _ _ bed last night.
3) The whale blew water _ _ _   _ _ the top of its head.
4) The little lamb could not walk _ _   _ _ _ _   _ _ the big sheep.
5) The ship was _ _ _ _ _ _ _ _ _ _ the jetty.
6) She found her book _ _ _ _ _ _ the cushion.

CONJUNCTIONS

Conjunctions are words used to join one thought to another thought. They join groups of words together, showing in what relation one group stands to the other.

Conjunctions are usually single words, like:-

   and   but   if   because   before   after   when   until

but sometimes they can be two words, like:-

either – or,   both – and,   whether – or,   even – if

Find the conjunctions in each of these sentences. Write your answers on your work pad.

1. Daniel is a talented and hard-working player.

2. Nobody likes Sharon because she is so bad-tempered.

3. Either that dog leaves this house or I do.

Conjunctions come before a reason, as in:

Billy drank a lot of water, because he was thirsty.

Conjunctions can show time, as in:

She has stopped riding her bike, since she last fell off.

Conjunctions can show the result of something, as in:

He did not do his homework, therefore the teacher kept him in after school.

The conjunctions are missing from these sentences. Write them on your work pad.

1) **The monkey climbed the tree easily,____ the elephant could not get off the ground.**

2) **____ its size, the crocodile is a good swimmer.**

3) **Fred opened the door ____ entered the house.**

SIMPLE SENTENCES

A simple sentence is one that has only one verb, which describes only one thing or idea.

The following are all simple sentences.

Kevin likes books.
A kennel is a little house for a dog.
The girls are playing netball.

DOUBLE SENTENCES

A double sentence is made up of two parts joined by a conjunction. In the following example, two separate sentences have been joined up by the word **and**, making one double sentence.

Eddie rang the bell. The door opened at once.

Eddie rang the bell and the door opened at once.

COMPLEX SENTENCES

A complex sentence has more than one verb in it and describes more than one thing or idea.

Here are some complex sentences.

The fox is very fond of hounds that can't smell.

Sophie has a new dress that fits her very well.

Sometimes, Susie wears a dress that belongs to her sister.

Four complex sentences have had their parts mixed up. Put the parts of each sentence together properly and write the answers on your work pad.

Polly is riding a bike that barks all night.

Mum hates any mouse that she is very proud of.

The cat has a new kitten that belongs to Ian.

Arthur complains about the dog that comes into the kitchen.

VERBS: PRESENT AND PAST TENSE

When a verb tells us about something that is happening at this moment, we say that it is in the **present tense**.

> **Present tense**   Mary washes her hair.

When the verb tells us about something that happened before now (in the past), we say it is in the **past tense**.

> **Past tense**   Mary washed her hair.

The sentences below are in the present tense. Write them in the past tense, telling us what happened yesterday.

1) I play football.
2) I fall over.
3) The referee helps me up.
4) I have a bath.
5) I go home.

ONE AND MORE THAN ONE

When a noun refers to one person, object or idea, it is **singular**.

When a noun refers to more than one person, object or idea, it is **plural**.

These nouns are **singular**:

apple   shoe   egg   girl   hand   thought

These nouns are **plural**:

apples   shoes   eggs   girls   hands   thoughts

The general rule for forming the plural of a noun is to add an **s** at the end.

One **snake** becomes two **snakes**.
One **skyscraper** becomes two **skyscrapers**.

If a word ends with **s**, **ss**, **sh**, **ch**, or **x**, we must add **es** to the end of the word to make it plural.

s　one atlas　—　two atlases
ss　one glass　—　two glasses
sh　one dash　—　two dashes
ch　one bench　—　two benches
x　one box　—　two boxes

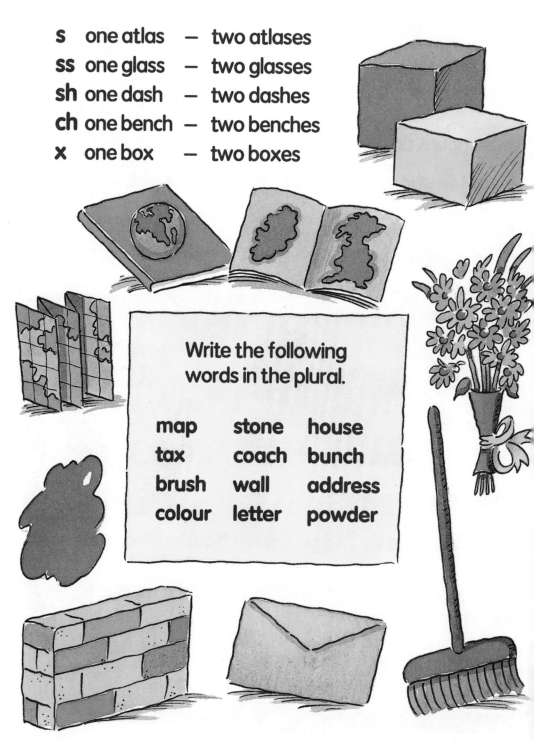

Write the following
words in the plural.

map　　stone　　house
tax　　coach　　bunch
brush　　wall　　address
colour　　letter　　powder

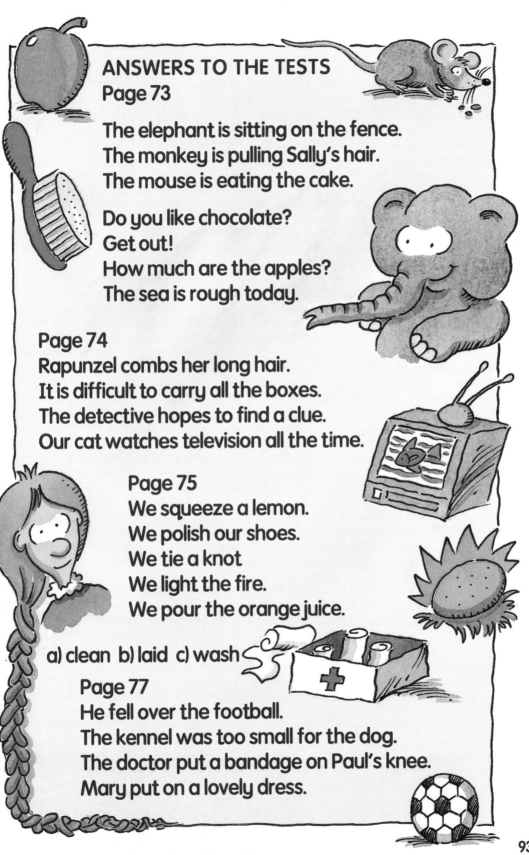

ANSWERS TO THE TESTS
Page 73

The elephant is sitting on the fence.
The monkey is pulling Sally's hair.
The mouse is eating the cake.

Do you like chocolate?
Get out!
How much are the apples?
The sea is rough today.

Page 74
Rapunzel combs her long hair.
It is difficult to carry all the boxes.
The detective hopes to find a clue.
Our cat watches television all the time.

Page 75
We squeeze a lemon.
We polish our shoes.
We tie a knot
We light the fire.
We pour the orange juice.

a) clean b) laid c) wash

Page 77
He fell over the football.
The kennel was too small for the dog.
The doctor put a bandage on Paul's knee.
Mary put on a lovely dress.

Page 79

1) subject – The elephant   object – a hat
2) subject – The fairy   object – her wings
3) subject – Snakes   object – legs
4) subject – Henry   object – ice cream

1) It cost her a lot of money.
2) They ate them.
3) She lets them sleep on her bed.

Page 80

1) thick   2) loud   3) close   4) quiet   5) yellow   6) heavy

1) friendly   little   2) shiny   roaring
3) haunted   dark   4) new   long   battered   old
5) muddy   torn

Page 81

1) ginger   2) Fierce   huge   3) Poor   serious   difficult
4) steaming   horrible

bro-ken   squ-are   flu-ffy   yel-low   sme-lly

Page 83

regularly   precisely   wealthily   powerfully
heavily   gladly   hungrily   noisily

1) Politely   2) bravely   3) greedily   4) beautifully

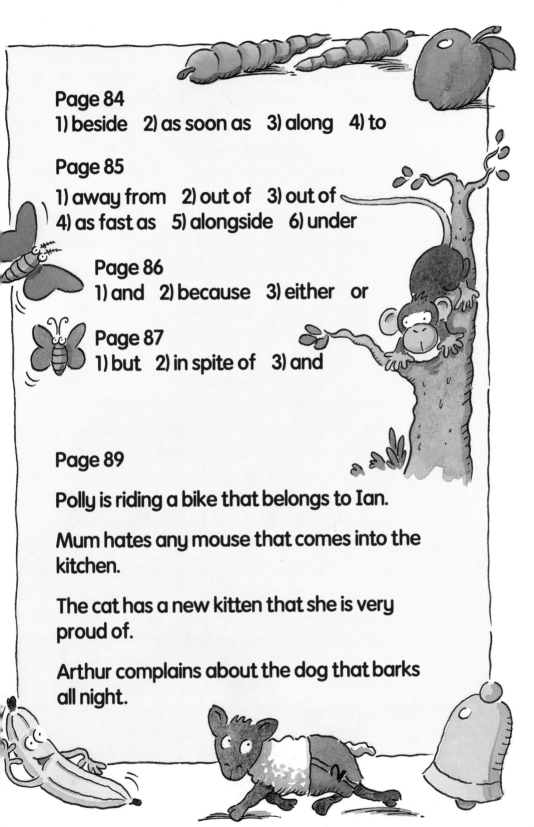

Page 84

1) beside   2) as soon as   3) along   4) to

Page 85

1) away from   2) out of   3) out of
4) as fast as   5) alongside   6) under

Page 86

1) and   2) because   3) either   or

Page 87

1) but   2) in spite of   3) and

Page 89

Polly is riding a bike that belongs to Ian.

Mum hates any mouse that comes into the kitchen.

The cat has a new kitten that she is very proud of.

Arthur complains about the dog that barks all night.

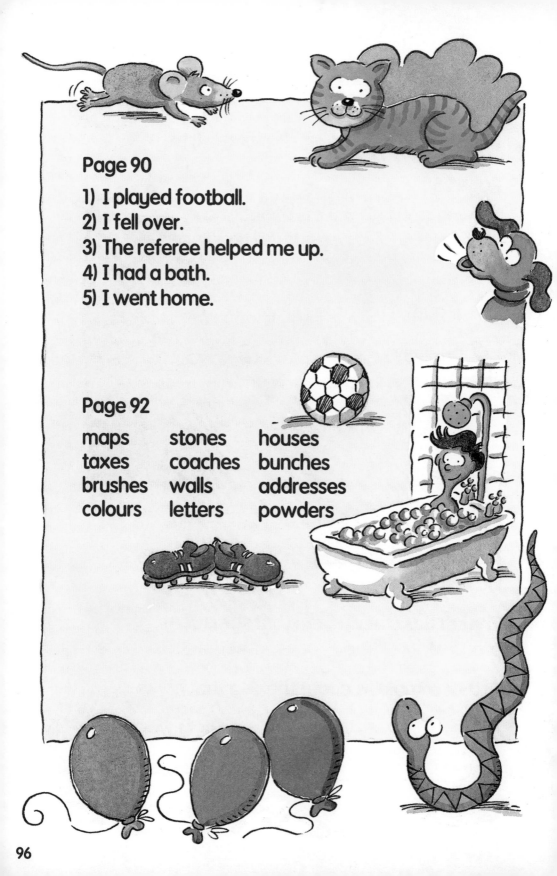

Page 90

1) I played football.
2) I fell over.
3) The referee helped me up.
4) I had a bath.
5) I went home.

Page 92

maps	stones	houses
taxes	coaches	bunches
brushes	walls	addresses
colours	letters	powders

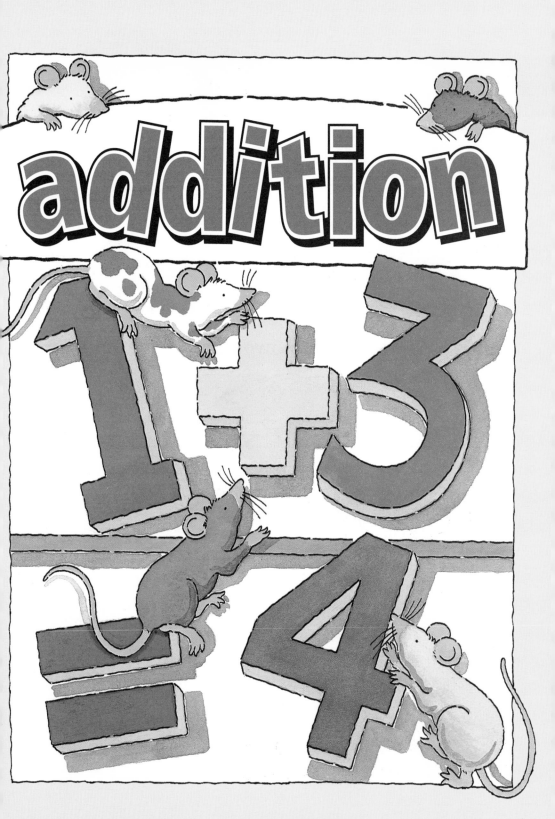

addition

$$1 + 3 = 4$$

This is a little mouse.

This is another little mouse.

Now there are two mice.

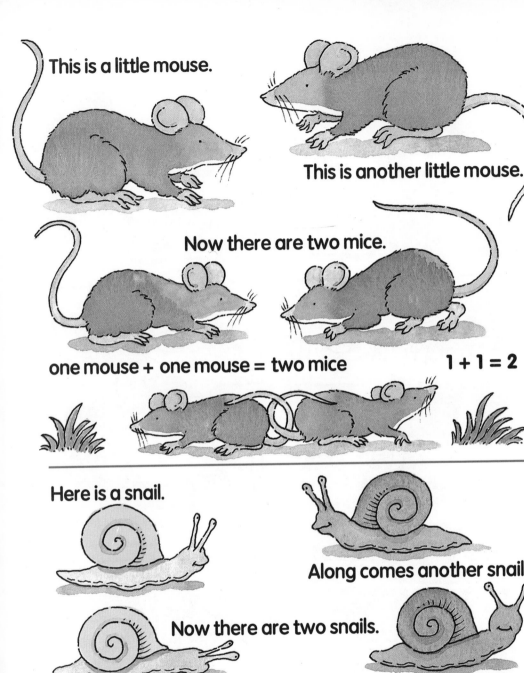

one mouse + one mouse = two mice

1 + 1 = 2

Here is a snail.

Along comes another snail.

Now there are two snails.

one snail + one snail = two snails

1 + 1 = 2

REMEMBER

1 + 1 = 2

Here is a rabbit.   Here is another rabbit.

Another rabbit hops up.

Now there are three rabbits.

one rabbit + one rabbit + one rabbit = three rabbits

1 + 1 + 1 = 3

One balloon.

Two more balloons float by.

Now there are three balloons.

one balloon + two balloons = three balloons   1 + 2 = 3

REMEMBER

| 1 + 1 + 1 = 3 | | 1 + 2 = 3 |

There is no mouse here.

Suddenly, a mouse appears.

Now there is one mouse here.

no mouse + one mouse = one mouse   **0 + 1 = 1**

There is no snail here.

Along come two snails.

Now there are two snails here.

no snail + two snails = two snails   **0 + 2 = 2**

REMEMBER | **0 + 1 = 1** | **0 + 2 = 2** |

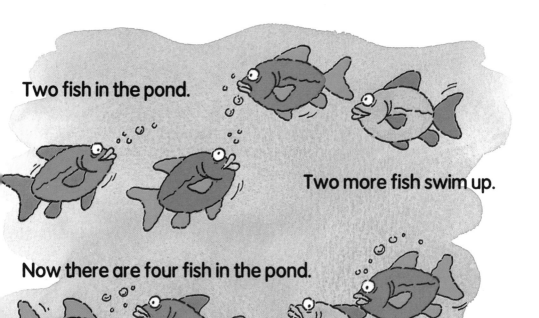

Two fish in the pond.

Two more fish swim up.

Now there are four fish in the pond.

two fish + two fish = four fish   **2 + 2 = 4**

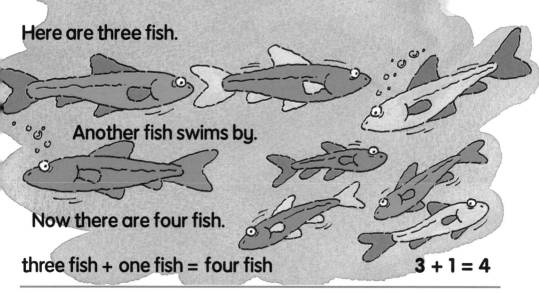

Here are three fish.

Another fish swims by.

Now there are four fish.

three fish + one fish = four fish   **3 + 1 = 4**

REMEMBER | **2 + 2 = 4** | **3 + 1 = 4** |

There are two balls in this box.

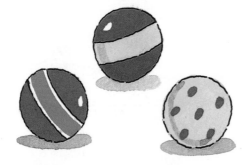

Here are three more balls.

Now there are five balls.

two balls + three balls = five balls   **2 + 3 = 5**

There are four oranges on the plate.

Here is another orange.

Now there are five oranges on the plate.

four oranges + one orange = five oranges   **4 + 1 = 5**

REMEMBER | **2 + 3 = 5** | | **4 + 1 = 5** |

Three little ducklings.

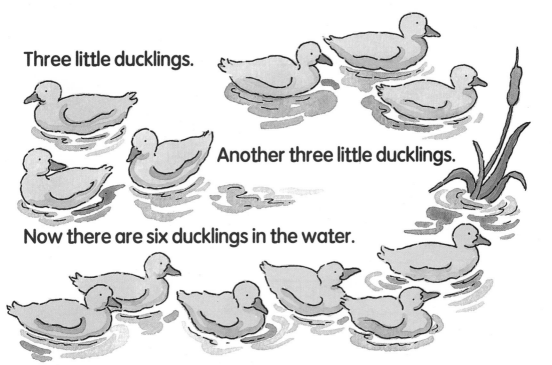

Another three little ducklings.

Now there are six ducklings in the water.

three ducklings + three ducklings = six ducklings

$$3 + 3 = 6$$

Here are four frogs.

Two more frogs hop by.

Now there are six frogs.

four frogs + two frogs = six frogs $4 + 2 = 6$

REMEMBER | $3 + 3 = 6$ | $4 + 2 = 6$ |

Can you load the sacks onto the right lorries?

Dominoes

The spots on each of these dominoes add up to 6.
Can you fill in the missing number groups?

There are seven dominoes shown here. If all the dominoes were completed, there would be one domino for each of the numbers from **0** to **6**. Can you decide what spots are missing, if any, from the dominoes that are not completed, so that you have a full set of numbers.

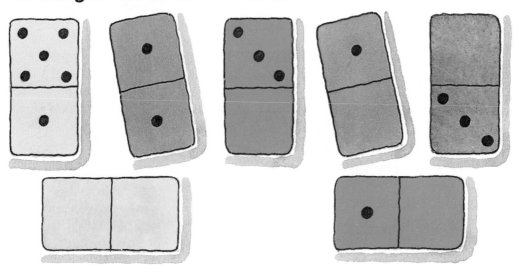

This bird's nest has four eggs in it.

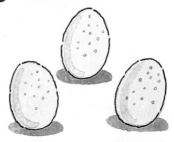

There are three eggs in this nest.

There are seven eggs altogether.

four eggs + three eggs = seven eggs   **4 + 3 = 7**

This black kitten is playing with five balls of wool.

This tabby kitten has two balls of wool.

Together, the kittens have seven balls of wool.

five balls of wool + two balls of wool = seven balls of wool

5 + 2 = 7

REMEMBER | **4 + 3 = 7** | | **5 + 2 = 7** |

How many dwarfs can you see in this picture?

How many dwarfs are in the woods?

If all the dwarfs are at home, how many dwarfs will be in the cottage?

Try to learn all the number bonds that make up seven. They are marked on the points of the snowflake.

1 + 6

0 + 7

3 + 4

2 + 5

7 + 0

4 + 3

6 + 1

5 + 2

There are five bees outside the beehive.

Along come three more bees.

Now there are eight bees outside the beehive.

five bees + three bees = eight bees   **5 + 3 = 8**

Here are six flags.

Here are two more flags.

There are eight flags altogether.

six flags + two flags = eight flags   **6 + 2 = 8**

REMEMBER | **5 + 3 = 8** | **6 + 2 = 8** |

There are eight sailing boats in the race.
Each boat should have a number on its sail,
but two boats have their numbers missing.

What are the missing numbers?

Try to learn all the number bonds that make up eight.
They are shown on the sails of the yachts.

Here are five bottles.

Here are another four bottles.

There are nine bottles altogether.

five bottles + four bottles = nine bottles   **5 + 4 = 9**

Tessa has three sweets.

Tommy has six sweets.

Altogether, they have nine sweets.

three sweets + six sweets = nine sweets   **3 + 6 = 9**

REMEMBER | **5 + 4 = 9** | | **3 + 6 = 9** |

Can you do these sums?

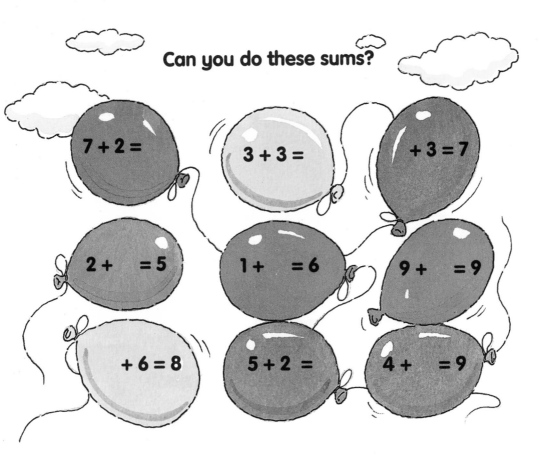

7 + 2 =

3 + 3 =

 + 3 = 7

2 +   = 5

1 +   = 6

9 +   = 9

 + 6 = 8

5 + 2 =

4 +   = 9

Try to learn all the number groups that make up nine.
They are shown below.

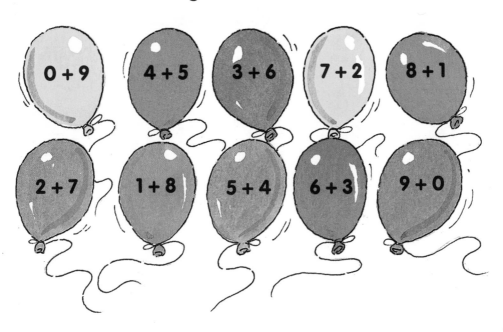

0 + 9

4 + 5

3 + 6

7 + 2

8 + 1

2 + 7

1 + 8

5 + 4

6 + 3

9 + 0

113

Up the ladders and down the snakes

These sums go up the ladders, from 1 to 9, and down the snakes, from 9 to 1. Can you fill in the missing numbers in each sum?

5 + ___ = 9	3 + ___ = 9	___ + 7 = 9	4 + 5 = ___
5 + ___ = 8	4 + ___ = 8	___ + 5 = 8	2 + 6 = ___
4 + ___ = 7	6 + ___ = 7	___ + 1 = 7	3 + 4 = ___
3 + ___ = 6	0 + ___ = 6	___ + 2 = 6	1 + 5 = ___
2 + ___ = 5	3 + ___ = 5	___ + 1 = 5	5 + 0 = ___
1 + ___ = 4	2 + ___ = 4	___ + 4 = 4	3 + 1 = ___
1 + ___ = 3	2 + ___ = 3	___ + 3 = 3	3 + 0 = ___
0 + ___ = 2	1 + ___ = 2	___ + 1 = 2	1 + 1 = ___
1 + ___ = 1	0 + ___ = 1	___ + 0 = 1	1 + 0 = ___

114

Collecting balls

Match the groups to the correct monkey.

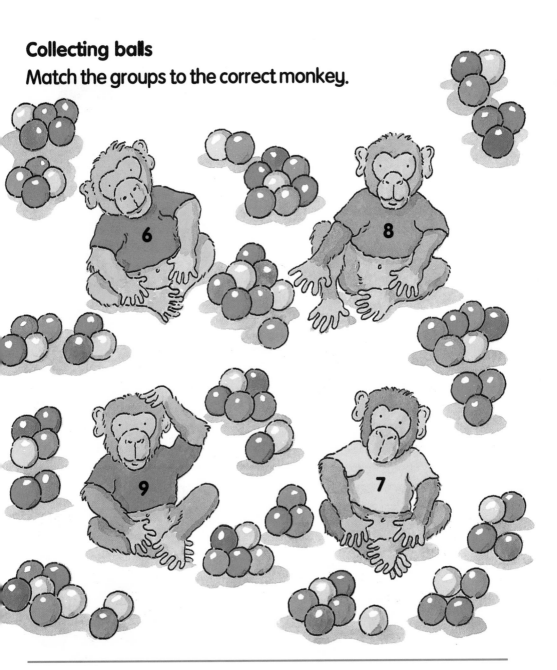

Count in 2s

| 2 – 4 – |
| 3 – 5 – |
| 5 – 7 – |
| 1 –   – 5 |
| – 4 – 6 |
| – 7 – 9 |

Tessa has four coins. Tommy has six coins.

Altogether, they have ten coins.

four coins + six coins = ten coins $4 + 6 = 10$

Tessa has seven coins. Tommy has three coins.

They have ten coins in all.

seven coins + three coins = ten coins $7 + 3 = 10$

REMEMBER | $4 + 6 = 10$ | $7 + 3 = 10$ |

Is there enough in the purse?

You need ten coins to buy a strawberry ice-cream, nine coins to buy a chocolate one, eight coins for a peppermint one, and seven coins for a vanilla ice-cream. Can you decide which ice-cream you can afford with the coins in each purse?

Try to learn all the number groups that make up ten. They are shown below.

This witch has seven broomsticks.

This witch has four broomsticks.

Altogether, the witches have eleven broomsticks.

seven broomsticks + four broomsticks = eleven broomsticks

$7 + 4 = 11$

The red witch has six pots.

The green witch has five pots.

They have eleven pots in all.

six pots + five pots = eleven pots

$6 + 5 = 11$

REMEMBER | $7 + 4 = 11$ | $6 + 5 = 11$

Tadpole totals

There are lots of tadpoles in these bowls. Can you work out how many there are in each bowl? How many bowls contain eleven tadpoles?

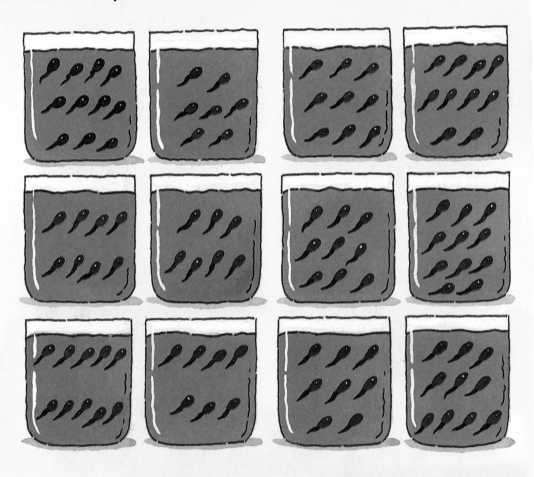

Count in 3s

3 – 6 –	1 – 4 –	5 – 8 –
4 – – 10	2 – – 8	– 6 – 9

There are five cherries on Tessa's plate.

There are seven cherries on Tommy's plate.

Altogether, they have twelve cherries.

five cherries + seven cherries = twelve cherries

5 + 7 = 12

There are eight cherries on this cake.

There are four cherries on this cake.

There are twelve cherries in all.

eight cherries + four cherries = twelve cherries

8 + 4 = 12

REMEMBER | **5 + 7 = 12** | **8 + 4 = 12** |

Can you do these sums?

+ 7 = 10

8 + 4 =

5 + 5 =

6 + 　 = 10

4 + 　 = 11

7 + 　 = 12

2 + 10 =

+ 6 = 11

3 + 8 =

8 + 2 =

2 + 9 =

+ 6 = 12

Count in 4s

| 1 – 5 – |
| 4 – 　 – 12 |
| 0 – 　 – 8 |
| 2 – 6 – |
| – 7 – 11 |

Magic Square

All the lines of numbers in this square, across, down, or diagonally, add up to 12. Can you fill in the missing numbers? The answer is printed upside-down at the foot of the page.

3	4	
		2
3	4	

The route to 12

Start at A and take whichever route gets to the answer at B.

A: Start   B: Finish

$$2 + 3 + \qquad 1 + 1$$
$$1 + 1 + 2 + 4 + 2 + 3 = 12$$
$$3 + 1 + \qquad 4 + 2$$

Odd numbers

Put a ring round each of the odd numbers in this list.

12   7   5   6   8   11   9   3   2   4

Even numbers

Put a ring round each of the even numbers in this list.

9   8   7   4   1   2   10   11   6   12

3	4	5
9	4	2
3	4	5

122

subtraction

Here are two little mice.

One little mouse goes down a mousehole.

Now there is only one mouse.

two mice – one mouse = one mouse $2 - 1 = 1$

There are two snails on the leaf.

One snail crawls away.

There is only one snail
on the leaf now.

two snails – one snail = one snail $2 - 1 = 1$

REMEMBER $\boxed{2 - 1 = 1}$

124

Here are three rabbits.

One rabbit hops away.

Then another rabbit hops away.

Now there is only one rabbit.

three rabbits – one rabbit – one rabbit = one rabbit

$$3 - 1 - 1 = 1$$

Three balloons.

Two balloons float away.

One balloon remains.

three balloons – two balloons = one balloon $3 - 2 = 1$

REMEMBER | $3 - 1 - 1 = 1$ | | $3 - 2 = 1$ |

One mouse eating cheese.

Along comes a cat.

Now there is no mouse eating cheese!

one mouse – one mouse = no mice $1 - 1 = 0$

Two birds on a wall.

Along comes a cat.
The birds fly away.

There are no birds on the wall!

two birds – two birds = no birds $2 - 2 = 0$

REMEMBER $1 - 1 = 0$ $2 - 2 = 0$

Four fish in a pond.

Two fish get caught in a net.

Only two fish are left in the pond.

four fish − two fish = two fish $4 - 2 = 2$

Four frogs on a lily leaf.

Three frogs dive into the water.

There is only one frog on the lily leaf.

four frogs − three frogs = one frog $4 - 3 = 1$

REMEMBER $4 - 2 = 2$ $4 - 3 = 1$

The clown is juggling with five balls.

He drops three balls.

Now the clown has only two balls in the air.

five balls – three balls = two balls

$5 - 3 = 2$

The jugglers have five clubs.

Four clubs fall to the ground.

The juggler is left with one club.

five clubs – four clubs = one club

$5 - 4 = 1$

REMEMBER $\boxed{5 - 3 = 2}$ $\boxed{5 - 4 = 1}$

Six socks on the washing line

The wind blows three socks away.

Now there are only three socks on the line.

six socks – three socks = three socks   **6 – 3 = 3**

Tommy has six sweets.

Tessa runs off with
four sweets.

Tommy is left with two sweets.

six sweets – four sweets = two sweets   **6 – 4 = 2**

REMEMBER | **6 – 3 = 3** | | **6 – 4 = 2** |

Submarine Subtraction

All the submarines shown here have take-away sums painted on their sides. In each group of submarines, two of the sums have the same answer. Can you draw a line between each pair that have the same answer?

How many buttons?

The toy soldiers are always getting their jackets mixed up. Each jacket has a different number of buttons. The captain has put take-away sums on their hats, so that each soldier will remember how many buttons there should be on his own jacket.

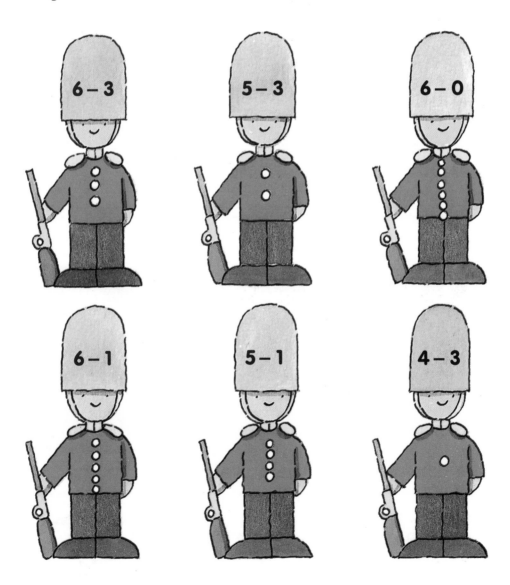

The little kitten has seven balls of wool.

The fat kitten runs off with three balls of wool.

Now the little kitten has four balls of wool.

seven balls of wool – three balls of wool =
four balls of wool.

7 – 3 = 4

The black cat has seven kittens.

Two kittens run away.

Now the black cat has five kittens left.

seven kittens – two kittens = five kittens.

7 – 2 = 5

REMEMBER | **7 – 3 = 4** | **7 – 2 = 5**

How many dwarfs go into the house?

How many dwarfs go off into the woods?

How many dwarfs are left behind in the little house?

Try to learn these sums when you take away numbers from seven.

7 – 7

7 – 0   7 – 6

7 – 1   7 – 5

7 – 2   7 – 4

7 – 3

0
7   1
6   7   2
5   3
4

This little dog has eight bones.

This big dog runs away with five bones.

The little dog has three bones now.

eight bones – five bones = three bones.   **8 – 5 = 3**

If the little dog has eight bones,

and the big dog runs away with four bones,

the little dog has four bones left.

eight bones – four bones = four bones   **8 – 4 = 4**

REMEMBER | **8 – 5 = 3** | **8 – 4 = 4** |

Taking Away Words

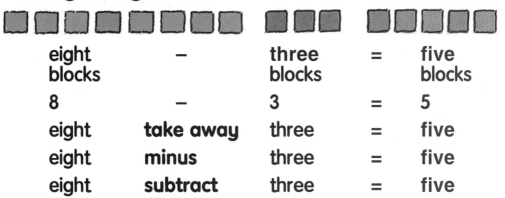

eight blocks	–	three blocks	=	five blocks
8	–	3	=	5
eight	**take away**	three	=	five
eight	**minus**	three	=	five
eight	**subtract**	three	=	five

This sign '–' and '**take away**' and '**minus**' and '**subtract**' all mean the same.

The answer in the sum above is the 'difference' between the first two numbers in each sum.

Try to learn these sums when you take away numbers from eight.

8 – 8 = 0   8 – 7 = 1   8 – 6 = 2

8 – 5 = 3   8 – 4 = 4   8 – 3 = 5

8 – 2 = 6   8 – 1 = 7   8 – 0 = 8

Nine coconuts on a tree.

A monkey picks five coconuts.

There are four coconuts still on the tree.

nine coconuts – five coconuts = four coconuts   **9 – 5 = 4**

The bird has laid nine eggs.

Three eggs hatch out.

Now the nest contains six eggs.

nine eggs – three eggs = six eggs.   **9 – 3 = 6**

REMEMBER | **9 – 5 = 4** | **9 – 3 = 6** |

Can you do these sums?

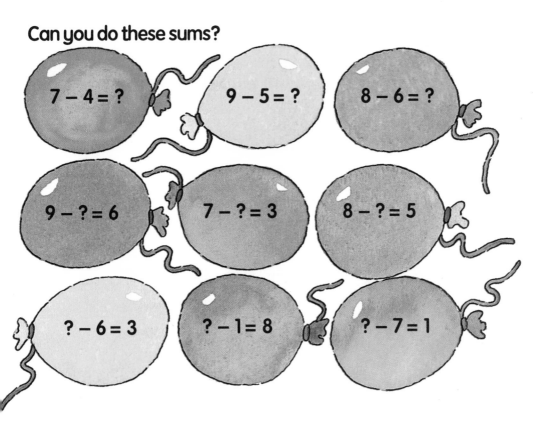

7 − 4 = ?

9 − 5 = ?

8 − 6 = ?

9 − ? = 6

7 − ? = 3

8 − ? = 5

? − 6 = 3

? − 1 = 8

? − 7 = 1

Try to learn these sums when you take away numbers from nine.

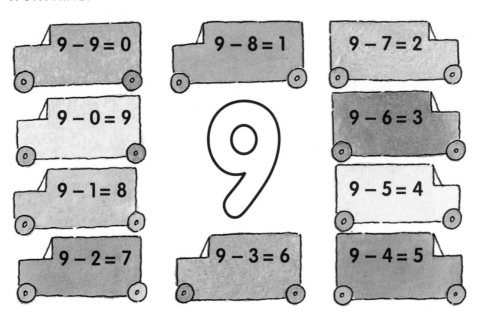

9 − 9 = 0

9 − 8 = 1

9 − 7 = 2

9 − 0 = 9

9

9 − 6 = 3

9 − 1 = 8

9 − 5 = 4

9 − 2 = 7

9 − 3 = 6

9 − 4 = 5

Sort the Sacks

Which sacks should be loaded onto each barrow?

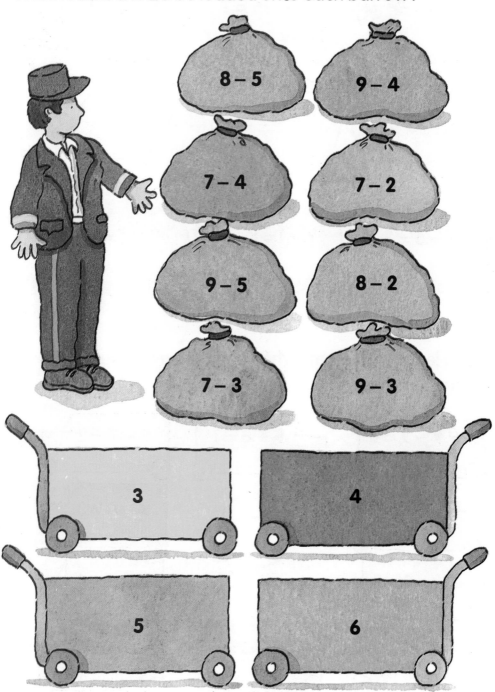

A taking away puzzle

Can you find the right way through this number puzzle?
You must move from square to square, sideways,
downwards, or diagonally, but you can only move onto
squares where the answer to the take away sum is two.

6 – 3	9 – 5	8 – 6	9 – 7	5 – 3	4 – 1	7 – 4
2 – 1	3 – 1	9 – 4	4 – 0	6 – 2	7 – 5	9 – 1
9 – 8	8 – 5	2 – 0	6 – 4	8 – 4	9 – 3	4 – 2
8 – 1	9 – 6	7 – 1	6 – 2	8 – 6	1 – 0	9 – 7
7 – 3	5 – 2	9 – 8	8 – 2	3 – 1	3 – 2	5 – 3
6 – 5	8 – 3	7 – 2	7 – 5	5 – 4	4 – 1	6 – 4

2

Tessa has ten coins.

She gives Tommy five coins.

Now she has five coins left. Tommy has five coins as well.

ten coins – five coins = five coins. **10 – 5 = 5**

Tessa has ten coins.

She gives Tommy four coins.

Now she has six coins.

ten coins – four coins = six coins **10 – 4 = 6**

REMEMBER | **10 – 5 = 5** | | **10 – 4 = 6** |

140

What's left in the purse?

Each purse contains ten coins.

Tessa buys two bottles and a box.
How many coins are left in the purse?

Tommy buys a box and a bottle.
How many coins are left in his purse?

How many coins will Tommy have left in his purse
if he buys another box?

Try to learn these sums when you take away numbers
from ten.

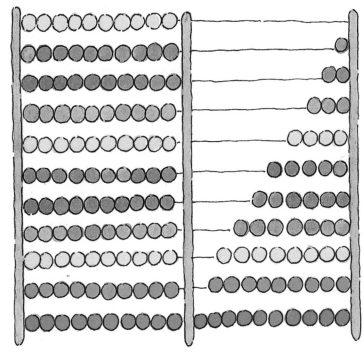

$$10 - 10 = 0$$
$$10 - 9 = 1$$
$$10 - 8 = 2$$
$$10 - 7 = 3$$
$$10 - 6 = 4$$
$$10 - 5 = 5$$
$$10 - 4 = 6$$
$$10 - 3 = 7$$
$$10 - 2 = 8$$
$$10 - 1 = 9$$
$$10 - 0 = 10$$

This witch has eleven broomsticks.

This witch flies away with seven broomsticks.

Now the witch has only four broomsticks.

eleven broomsticks – seven broomsticks = four broomsticks.

11 – 7 = 4

The red witch has eleven pots.

The green witch goes away with six pots.

Now the red witch has five pots.

eleven pots – six pots = five pots.

11 – 6 = 5

REMEMBER | **11 – 7 = 4** | **11 – 6 = 5**

If there are nine skittles standing up and four skittles get knocked down, how many remain standing?

If there are ten lighted candles on the cake and six candles are blown out, how many are still alight?

Take away 2s
4 – 2 – ?, 10 – 8 – ?, 9 – 7 – ?, 5 – ? – 1, ? – 6 – 4

Take away 3s
10 – 7 – ?, 8 – ? – 2, ? – 6 – 3 , ? – 3 – 0, 10 – ? – 4

There are twelve petals on the flower.

If seven petals blow away,

there will be five petals left on the flower.

twelve petals – seven petals = five petals   **12 – 7 = 5**

There are twelve bananas on the tree.
If the monkey eats four bananas,

there will be eight bananas left on the tree.

twelve bananas – four bananas = eight bananas

12 – 4 = 8

REMEMBER | **12 – 7 = 5** | **12 – 4 = 8**

Can you do these sums?

12 – 10 = ?

12 – 9 = ?

12 – 4 = ?

12 – ? = 1

12 – 5 = ?

12 – ? = 6

12 – ? = 4

12 – ? = 9

? – 7 = 5

? – 9 = 2

? – 7 = 3

? – 8 = 4

Take away 4s
12 – 8 – ?, 11 – ? – 3, ? – 6 – 2, 9 – ? – 1, ? – 4 – 0

A taking away riddle

What has eight legs and three heads?

Work out the answers to these sums and then, using the answers and the code, fill in the missing letters.

1) 12 − 2 ☐   2) 11 − 2 ☐

3) 12 − 4 ☐   4) 10 − 3 ☐   5) 9 − 3 ☐

6) 12 − 7 ☐   7) 7 − 3 ☐   8) 8 − 5 ☐

9) 9 − 7 ☐   10) 12 − 11 ☐   11) 12 − 9 ☐

12) 10 − 9 ☐   13) 12 − 3 ☐   14) 11 − 8 ☐

E = 9	W = 10
A = 7	T = 8
S = 5	M = 6
O = 3	R = 4
N = 1	H = 2

− − −   − − −   − −   −   − − − − −
3) 1) 8)   5) 13) 10)   11) 12)   4)   9) 14) 7) 6) 2)

times tables

2 times table

0	× 2	=	0
1	× 2	=	2
2	× 2	=	4
3	× 2	=	6
4	× 2	=	8
5	× 2	=	10
6	× 2	=	12
7	× 2	=	14
8	× 2	=	16
9	× 2	=	18
10	× 2	=	20
11	× 2	=	22
12	× 2	=	24

Jack has 2 balloons.　　　　John has 2 balloons.

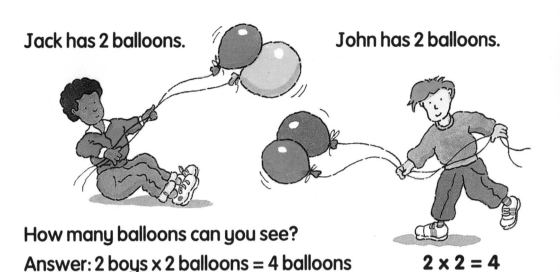

How many balloons can you see?

Answer: 2 boys x 2 balloons = 4 balloons　　**2 x 2 = 4**

Jane has 2 gloves.　　Jenny has 2 gloves.　　Jill has 2 gloves.

There are 3 girls. Each girl has 2 gloves.

How many gloves can you see?

Answer: 3 girls x 2 gloves = 6 gloves　　**3 x 2 = 6**

Here are 2 girls, Jane and Jenny. Each girl has 3 gloves.

How many gloves can you see?

Answer: 2 girls x 3 gloves = 6 gloves　　**2 x 3 = 6**

2 x 3 = 6 is the same as 3 x 2 = 6

3 times table

$$0 \times 3 = 0$$
$$1 \times 3 = 3$$
$$2 \times 3 = 6$$
$$3 \times 3 = 9$$
$$4 \times 3 = 12$$
$$5 \times 3 = 15$$
$$6 \times 3 = 18$$
$$7 \times 3 = 21$$
$$8 \times 3 = 24$$
$$9 \times 3 = 27$$
$$10 \times 3 = 30$$
$$11 \times 3 = 33$$
$$12 \times 3 = 36$$

The black monkey has 3 coconuts.

The brown monkey has 3 coconuts.

The grey monkey has 3 coconuts.

There are 3 monkeys. Each monkey has 3 coconuts.

How many coconuts are there?

Answer: 3 monkeys x 3 coconuts = 9 coconuts   **3 x 3 = 9**

Here are 4 caterpillars. Each caterpillar has 3 leaves.

How many leaves are there?

Answer: 4 caterpillars x 3 leaves = 12 leaves   **4 x 3 = 12**

Here are 3 caterpillars. Each caterpillar has 4 leaves.

How many leaves are there?

Answer: 3 caterpillars x 4 leaves = 12 leaves   **3 x 4 = 12**

3 x 4 = 12 is the same as **4 x 3 = 12**

4 times table

$$0 \times 4 = 0$$
$$1 \times 4 = 4$$
$$2 \times 4 = 8$$
$$3 \times 4 = 12$$
$$4 \times 4 = 16$$
$$5 \times 4 = 20$$
$$6 \times 4 = 24$$
$$7 \times 4 = 28$$
$$8 \times 4 = 32$$
$$9 \times 4 = 36$$
$$10 \times 4 = 40$$
$$11 \times 4 = 44$$
$$12 \times 4 = 48$$

The black sheep has 4 legs.

The white sheep has 4 legs.

The grey sheep has 4 legs.

The sheep with horns has 4 legs.

There are 4 sheep. Each sheep has 4 legs.

How many legs can you see?

Answer: 4 sheep x 4 legs = 16 legs   **4 x 4 = 16**

Here are 5 dogs. Each dog has 4 bones.

How many bones are there?

Answer: 5 dogs x 4 bones = 20 bones   **5 x 4 = 20**

Here are 4 dogs. Each dog has 5 bones.

How many bones are there?

Answer: 4 dogs x 5 bones = 20 bones   **4 x 5 = 20**
4 x 5 = 20 is the same as 5 x 4 = 20

5 times table

0	×	5	=	0
1	×	5	=	5
2	×	5	=	10
3	×	5	=	15
4	×	5	=	20
5	×	5	=	25
6	×	5	=	30
7	×	5	=	35
8	×	5	=	40
9	×	5	=	45
10	×	5	=	50
11	×	5	=	55
12	×	5	=	60

The white mouse has 5 pieces of cheese.

The black mouse has 5 pieces of cheese.

The grey mouse has 5 pieces of cheese.

The brown mouse has 5 pieces of cheese.

The spotted mouse has 5 pieces of cheese.

There are 5 mice. Each mouse has 5 pieces of cheese.
How many pieces of cheese are there?

Answer: 5 mice x 5 pieces of cheese =
25 pieces of cheese   **5 x 5 = 25**

Here are 6 cats. Each cat has 5 kittens.

How many kittens are there?

Answer: 6 cats x 5 kittens = 30 kittens

6 x 5 = 30

6 x 5 = 30 is the same as **5 x 6 = 30**

6 times table

$$0 \times 6 = 0$$
$$1 \times 6 = 6$$
$$2 \times 6 = 12$$
$$3 \times 6 = 18$$
$$4 \times 6 = 24$$
$$5 \times 6 = 30$$
$$6 \times 6 = 36$$
$$7 \times 6 = 42$$
$$8 \times 6 = 48$$
$$9 \times 6 = 54$$
$$10 \times 6 = 60$$
$$11 \times 6 = 66$$
$$12 \times 6 = 72$$

The red hen has laid 6 eggs.

The white hen has laid 6 eggs.

The brown hen has laid 6 eggs.

The yellow hen has laid 6 eggs.

The black hen has laid 6 eggs.

The speckled hen has laid 6 eggs.

There are 6 hens. Each hen has laid 6 eggs.

How many eggs can you see?

Answer: 6 hens x 6 eggs = 36 eggs   **6 x 6 = 36**

There are 7 ducks and each duck has 6 ducklings.

How many ducklings are there?

Answer: 7 ducks x 6 ducklings = 42 ducklings   **7 x 6 = 42**

There are 6 ducks and each
duck has 7 ducklings.

How many ducklings are there?

Answer: 6 ducks x 7 ducklings = 42 ducklings
6 x 7 = 42
6 x 7 = 42 is the same as **7 x 6 = 42**

7 times table

$0 \times 7 = 0$

$1 \times 7 = 7$

$2 \times 7 = 14$

$3 \times 7 = 21$

$4 \times 7 = 28$

$5 \times 7 = 35$

$6 \times 7 = 42$

$7 \times 7 = 49$

$8 \times 7 = 56$

$9 \times 7 = 63$

$10 \times 7 = 70$

$11 \times 7 = 77$

$12 \times 7 = 84$

The brown puppy has 7 balls.

The black puppy has 7 balls.

The white puppy has 7 balls.

The golden puppy has 7 balls.

The shaggy puppy has 7 balls.

The small puppy has 7 balls.

The biggest puppy has 7 balls.

There are 7 puppies. Each puppy has 7 balls.

How many balls are there?

Answer: 7 puppies x 7 balls = 49 balls   **7 x 7 = 49**

There are 8 frogs and each frog has 7 tadpoles.

How many tadpoles are there?

Answer: 8 frogs x 7 tadpoles = 56 tadpoles   **8 x 7 = 56**

8 x 7 = 56 is the same as **7 x 8 = 56**

8 times table

$0 \times 8 = 0$

$1 \times 8 = 8$

$2 \times 8 = 16$

$3 \times 8 = 24$

$4 \times 8 = 32$

$5 \times 8 = 40$

$6 \times 8 = 48$

$7 \times 8 = 56$

$8 \times 8 = 64$

$9 \times 8 = 72$

$10 \times 8 = 80$

$11 \times 8 = 88$

$12 \times 8 = 96$

The octopus has eight arms.

Here are another 7 octopuses. Each one has 8 arms.

There are 8 octopuses. Each octopus has 8 arms.

How many arms are there?

Answer: 8 octopuses x 8 arms = 64 arms   **8 x 8 = 64**

Here are 9 dominoes. Each domino has 8 spots on it.

How many spots can you see?

Answer: 9 dominoes x 8 spots = 72 spots   **9 x 8 = 72**

9 x 8 = 72 is the same as **8 x 9 = 72**

9 times table

$$0 \times 9 = 0$$
$$1 \times 9 = 9$$
$$2 \times 9 = 18$$
$$3 \times 9 = 27$$
$$4 \times 9 = 36$$
$$5 \times 9 = 45$$
$$6 \times 9 = 54$$
$$7 \times 9 = 63$$
$$8 \times 9 = 72$$
$$9 \times 9 = 81$$
$$10 \times 9 = 90$$
$$11 \times 9 = 99$$
$$12 \times 9 = 108$$

The flower has 9 petals on it.

Here are another 8 flowers.

Each flower has 9 petals.

There are 9 flowers. Each flower has 9 petals.

How many petals can you see?

Answer: 9 flowers x 9 petals = 81 petals   **9 x 9 = 81**

Here are 10 crates. Each crate has 9 lemonade bottles in it.

How many lemonade bottles are there?

Answer: 10 crates x 9 bottles = 90 bottles   **10 x 9 = 90**

10 x 9 = 90 is the same as **9 x 10 = 90**

10 times table

$$0 \times 10 = 0$$
$$1 \times 10 = 10$$
$$2 \times 10 = 20$$
$$3 \times 10 = 30$$
$$4 \times 10 = 40$$
$$5 \times 10 = 50$$
$$6 \times 10 = 60$$
$$7 \times 10 = 70$$
$$8 \times 10 = 80$$
$$9 \times 10 = 90$$
$$10 \times 10 = 100$$
$$11 \times 10 = 110$$
$$12 \times 10 = 120$$

This is a telephone.

It has 10 numbers on it.

Here are another 9 telephones.

Each telephone has 10 numbers on it.

There are 10 telephones. Each telephone has 10 numbers.

How many numbers are there?

Answer: 10 telephones x 10 numbers = 100 numbers

$$10 \times 10 = 100$$

If there were 11 rabbits and each rabbit had 10 carrots,

how many carrots would there be?

Answer: 11 rabbits x 10 carrots = 110 carrots $11 \times 10 = 110$

$11 \times 10 = 110$ is the same as $10 \times 11 = 110$

11 times table

0	×	11	=	0
1	×	11	=	11
2	×	11	=	22
3	×	11	=	33
4	×	11	=	44
5	×	11	=	55
6	×	11	=	66
7	×	11	=	77
8	×	11	=	88
9	×	11	=	99
10	×	11	=	110
11	×	11	=	121
12	×	11	=	132

Here are 11 sweets.

Here are another 10 piles each with 11 sweets.

There are 11 piles. Each pile has 11 sweets.

How many sweets are there?

Answer: 11 piles x 11 sweets = 121 sweets

11 x 11 = 121

If there were 12 ants and each ant had a pile of 11 seeds, how many seeds would there be?

Answer: 12 ants x 11 seeds = 132 seeds   **12 x 11 = 132**

12 x 11 = 132 is the same as 11 x 12 = 132

12 times table

0	×	12	=	0
1	×	12	=	12
2	×	12	=	24
3	×	12	=	36
4	×	12	=	48
5	×	12	=	60
6	×	12	=	72
7	×	12	=	84
8	×	12	=	96
9	×	12	=	108
10	×	12	=	120
11	×	12	=	132
12	×	12	=	144

This clock has 12 numbers on its face.

Here are another 11 clocks. Each clock has 12 numbers.

There are 12 clocks. Each clock has 12 numbers.

How many numbers can you see on the clocks?

Answer: 12 clocks x 12 numbers = 144 numbers

$$12 \times 12 = 144$$

If there were 7 snowflakes and each
snowflake had 12 points,

how many points would there be?

Answer: 7 snowflakes x 12 points = 84 points $7 \times 12 = 84$
$7 \times 12 = 84$ is the same as $12 \times 7 = 84$

Times table sums

The answers are at the foot of the page

1) 2 boys: each boy has 7 balloons.
How many balloons altogether?
$2 \times 7 = ?$

2) 3 monkeys: each monkey has 6 coconuts.
How many coconuts altogether?
$3 \times 6 = ?$

3) 6 sheep: each sheep has 4 legs.
How many legs in all?
$6 \times 4 = ?$

4) 4 mice: each mouse has 5 pieces of cheese.
How many pieces of cheese altogether?
$4 \times 5 = ?$

5) 5 hens: each hen has laid 8 eggs.
How many eggs in all?
$5 \times 8 = ?$

6) 7 octopuses: each octopus has 8 arms.
How many arms altogether?
$7 \times 8 = ?$

6) $7 \times 8 = 56$ 5) $5 \times 8 = 40$ 4) $4 \times 5 = 20$
3) $6 \times 4 = 24$ 2) $3 \times 6 = 18$ 1) $2 \times 7 = 14$

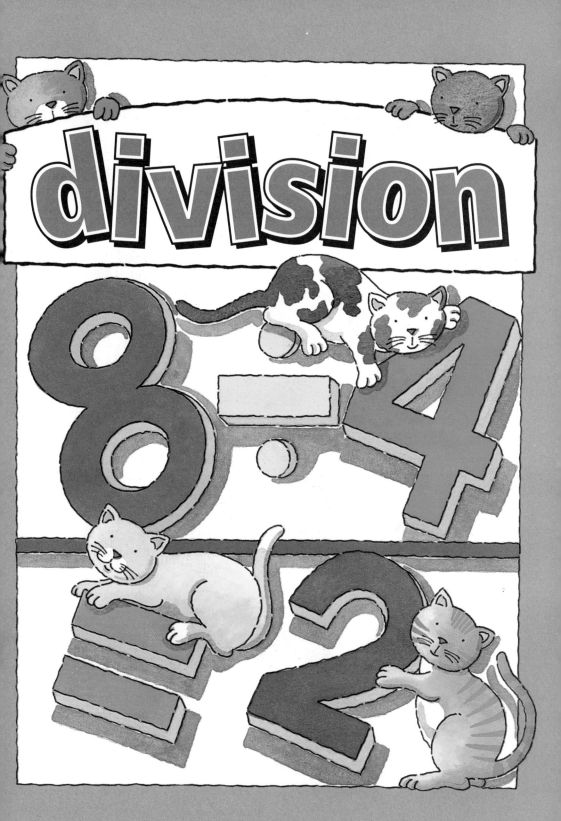

division

8 ÷ 4 ÷ 2

Here are two balloons.

This is Jack.

This is John.

If we share the balloons between the two boys, each boy will have one balloon.

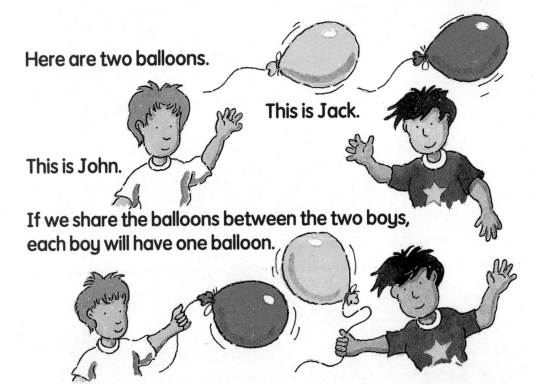

two balloons ÷ two boys = one balloon each   **2 ÷ 2 = 1**

Here are three hats.

Here are three girls.

If we share the hats between the girls, each girl will have one hat.

three hats ÷ three girls = one hat for each girl   **3 ÷ 3 = 1**

REMEMBER: Dividing means **sharing equally.**
            Any number divided by itself equals **1.**

1 ÷ 1 = 1   **2 ÷ 2 = 1**   **3 ÷ 3 = 1**   **4 ÷ 4 = 1**

Here are four balloons.

Here are two boys.

If we share the balloons between the two boys,
each boy will have two balloons.

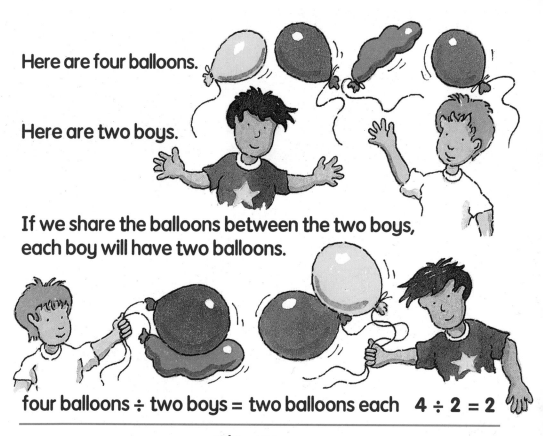

four balloons ÷ two boys = two balloons each   **4 ÷ 2 = 2**

Here are eight gloves.

Here are two girls.

If we share the gloves between the girls,
each girl will have four gloves.

eight gloves ÷ two girls = four gloves each   **8 ÷ 2 = 4**

REMEMBER: You can only divide even numbers by **2**.
You cannot divide odd numbers by **2**.

2 ÷ 2 = 1   6 ÷ 2 = 3   8 ÷ 2 = 4   5 ÷ 2 = no

173

Here are six coconuts.

Here are three monkeys.

If they share the coconuts equally,
each monkey will have two coconuts.

six coconuts ÷ three monkeys = two coconuts each

6 ÷ 3 = 2

If there are six coconuts,

and two monkeys,

each monkey will have three coconuts.

six coconuts ÷ two monkeys = three coconuts each

6 ÷ 2 = 3

REMEMBER: Any number divided by **1** remains the same.

6 ÷ 1 = 6   5 ÷ 1 = 5   2 ÷ 1 = 2   1 ÷ 1 = 1

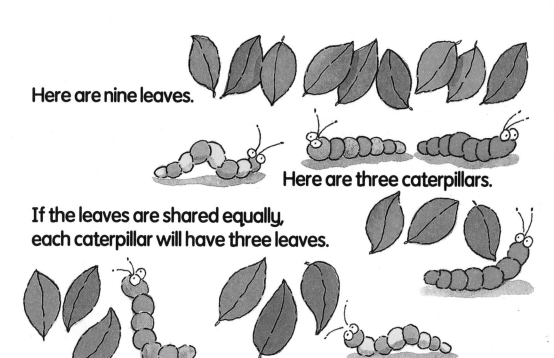

Here are nine leaves.

Here are three caterpillars.

If the leaves are shared equally,
each caterpillar will have three leaves.

nine leaves ÷ three caterpillars = three leaves each

9 ÷ 3 = 3

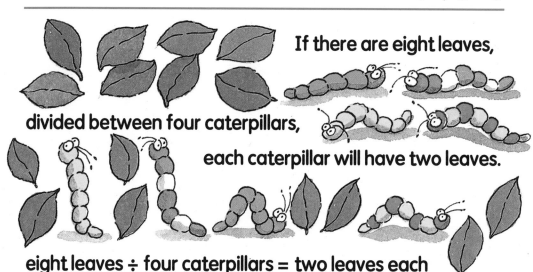

If there are eight leaves,

divided between four caterpillars,

each caterpillar will have two leaves.

eight leaves ÷ four caterpillars = two leaves each

8 ÷ 4 = 2

REMEMBER: When we divide any number by two,
each part is **half** of the original number.

8 ÷ 2 = 4   6 ÷ 2 = 3   4 ÷ 2 = 2   2 ÷ 2 = 1

There are ten bones on the ground,

and five dogs to share them.

Each dog will have two bones.

ten bones ÷ five dogs = two bones each   10 ÷ 5 = 2

There are twelve bones,

and four dogs to share them.

Each dog will have three bones.

twelve bones ÷ four dogs = three bones each   12 ÷ 4 = 3

REMEMBER:
10 ÷ 5 = 2   10 ÷ 2 = 5   12 ÷ 4 = 3

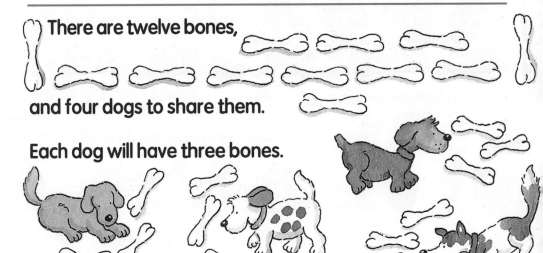

If we divide fourteen pieces of cheese

between seven mice,

each mouse will have two pieces of cheese.

fourteen pieces of cheese ÷ seven mice =
two pieces of cheese for each mouse   **14 ÷ 7 = 2**

If we divide twenty-one pieces of cheese,

between seven mice,

each mouse will have three pieces of cheese.

twenty-one pieces of cheese ÷ seven mice =
three pieces of cheese for each mouse   **21 ÷ 7 = 3**

REMEMBER:
14 ÷ 7 = 2   14 ÷ 2 = 7   21 ÷ 7 = 3

Parachute puzzle

Which plane has each parachute come from?
Find out by answering the sums on the sides of the planes.

Sharing sums

The answers are at the foot of the page.

1) Share 10 coconuts between 5 monkeys.
   How many coconuts for each monkey?

2) Share 9 balloons between 3 boys.
   How many balloons for each boy?

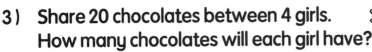

3) Share 20 chocolates between 4 girls.
   How many chocolates will each girl have?

4) Share 30 eggs between 6 nests.
   How many eggs in each nest?

5) Share 24 fish between 4 fishbowls.
   How many fish in each bowl?

6) Share 40 carrots between 5 rabbits.
   How many carrots can each rabbit eat?

Answers:

6) $40 \div 5 = 8$ 5) $24 \div 4 = 6$ 4) $30 \div 6 = 5$

3) $20 \div 4 = 5$ 2) $9 \div 3 = 3$ 1) $10 \div 5 = 2$

Here are twenty-four bottles.

Each of these crates will hold six bottles.

How many crates will we need for them?

twenty-four bottles ÷ six (bottles in a crate) =
four crates   **24 ÷ 6 = 4**

If we have thirty bottles, we will fill five crates.

thirty bottles ÷ six (bottles in a crate) = five crates
                                              30 ÷ 6 = 5

REMEMBER: Only numbers which end with a **5** or a **0** can
be divided by **5.**

5   10   15   20   25   30   35   40   45   50   55   60

180

Here are thirty-six eggs.

Each of these hens has laid the same number of eggs.

How many eggs has each hen laid?
thirty-six eggs ÷ six hens =
six eggs for each hen

$36 \div 6 = 6$

Here are forty-two ducklings.

If there are seven ducks,

how many ducklings belong to each duck?

forty-two ducklings ÷ seven ducks =
six ducklings for each duck

$42 \div 7 = 6$

REMEMBER:

$36 \div 6 = 6$ $42 \div 7 = 6$

181

If there are forty-nine carrots,

and seven hungry rabbits,

how many carrots will each rabbit have?

forty-nine carrots ÷ seven rabbits =
seven carrots for each rabbit

49 ÷ 7 = 7

These fifty-six tadpoles

belong to these eight frogs.

How many tadpoles does each frog have?

fifty-six tadpoles ÷ eight frogs =
seven tadpoles for each frog

56 ÷ 8 = 7

REMEMBER:

49 ÷ 7 = 7   56 ÷ 8 = 7

There are sixty-four bees in this swarm.

There are eight beehives here.

How many bees will go into each beehive?

sixty-four bees ÷ eight beehives =
eight bees in each beehive

64 ÷ 8 = 8

If there are seventy-two bees in the swarm,

and eight beehives,

how many bees will there be in each beehive?

seventy-two bees ÷ eight beehives =
nine bees in each beehive

72 ÷ 8 = 9

REMEMBER:

64 ÷ 8 = 8   72 ÷ 8 = 9

Can you do these sums?
The answers are at the foot of the page.

1) 7 ÷ 7

2) 9 ÷ 1

3) 12 ÷ 3

4) 14 ÷ 2

5) 20 ÷ 4

6) 24 ÷ 6

7) 28 ÷ 4

8) 30 ÷ 5

9) 36 ÷ 6

10) 42 ÷ 7

11) 45 ÷ 5

12) 49 ÷ 7

13) 56 ÷ 8

14) 64 ÷ 8

15) 72 ÷ 9

Answers:

9)6   10)6   11)9   12)7   13)7   14)8   15)8

1)1   2)9   3)4   4)7   5)5   6)4   7)7   8)6

184

Can you fill in the missing numbers?

The answers are at the foot of the page.

1)   5 ÷ ☐ = 1

2)   3 ÷ ☐ = 3

3)   8 ÷ ☐ = 4

4)   6 ÷ ☐ = 2

5)   ☐ ÷ 7 = 3

6)   ☐ ÷ 6 = 4

7)   ☐ ÷ 9 = 5

8)   ☐ ÷ 8 = 6

9)   ☐ ÷ 5 = 5

10) 36 ÷ ☐ = 4

11) 66 ÷ ☐ = 11

12) 54 ÷ ☐ = 6

13) ☐ ÷ 7 = 9

14) ☐ ÷ 4 = 12

15) 49 ÷ ☐ = 7

185

If we share seventy chocolates

between ten children,

how many chocolates would each child get?

seventy chocolates ÷ ten children =
seven chocolates each   **70 ÷ 10 = 7**

If sixty chocolates are divided,

between ten children,

each child will have six chocolates.

sixty chocolates ÷ ten children = six chocolates each
                                        60 ÷ 10 = 6

REMEMBER:

Only numbers which end with a **0** can be divided by **10**.

10   20   30   40   50   60   70   80   90   100

If we divide twelve balls

between six boxes,

each box will have two balls.

twelve balls ÷ six boxes = two balls in each box

12 ÷ 6 = 2

If we divide twelve balls

between two boxes,

each box will have six balls.

twelve balls ÷ two boxes = six balls in each box

12 ÷ 2 = 6

REMEMBER:

12 ÷ 6 = 2   **12 ÷ 2 = 6**   **24 ÷ 6 = 4**   **24 ÷ 4 = 6**

We can divide some numbers in lots of different ways.

Here are 24 beads divided by twenty-four. $24 \div 24 = 1$

Here are 24 beads divided by twelve. $24 \div 12 = 2$

Here are 24 beads divided by six. $24 \div 6 = 4$

Here are 24 beads divided by four. $24 \div 4 = 6$

Here are 24 beads divided by two. $24 \div 2 = 12$

Here are 24 beads divided by one. $24 \div 1 = 24$

Here is another number that can be divided in different ways.

Here are 30 sweets divided by thirty.   **30 ÷ 30 = 1**

Here are 30 sweets divided by fifteen.   **30 ÷ 15 = 2**

Here are 30 sweets divided by ten.   **30 ÷ 10 = 3**

Here are 30 sweets divided by five.   **30 ÷ 5 = 6**

Here are 30 sweets divided by two.   **30 ÷ 2 = 15**

Here are 30 sweets divided by one.   **30 ÷ 1 = 30**

189

Dividing and sharing quiz

Can you answer these questions?
Look at the foot of the page to see if you are right.

A) 36 flowers

1) How many 12s?   2) How many 9s?

3) How many 6s?   4) How many 4s?

5) How many 3s?   6) How many 2s?

B) 40 arrows

1) How many 20s?   2) How many 10s?

3) How many 8s?   4) How many 5s?

5) How many 4s?   6) How many 2s?

C) 48 rockets

1) How many 24s?   2) How many 16s?

3) How many 12s?   4) How many 8s?

5) How many 6s?   6) How many 4s?

7) How many 3s?   8) How many 2s?

Answers:

C) 1) 2 2) 3 3) 4 4) 6 5) 8 6) 12 7) 16 8) 24

B) 1) 2 2) 4 3) 5 4) 8 5) 10 6) 20

A) 1) 3 2) 4 3) 6 4) 9 5) 12 6) 18

190

Camel calculations

This camel has six loads to carry. Each load is made up of 4 boxes. Work out the sums on the side of each box and add them together to see what each load weighs. The camel cannot carry a load that weighs more than 20. Which load is too heavy for it?

18 ÷ 6	12 ÷ 2	36 ÷ 6	32 ÷ 8
24 ÷ 4	15 ÷ 3	27 ÷ 9	24 ÷ 4
25 ÷ 5	18 ÷ 9	9 ÷ 3	40 ÷ 8
20 ÷ 5	21 ÷ 3	49 ÷ 7	12 ÷ 2
30 ÷ 6	14 ÷ 2	14 ÷ 2	24 ÷ 8
10 ÷ 5	28 ÷ 7	45 ÷ 9	15 ÷ 5

A · B · C · D · E · F

Answers:

Load E is too heavy for the camel to carry

A) $3 + 6 + 6 + 5 = 20$
B) $5 + 2 + 4 + 7 = 18$
C) $5 + 7 + 2 + 4 = 18$
D) $6 + 4 + 3 + 6 = 19$
E) $3 + 5 + 7 + 6 = 21$
F) $7 + 3 + 5 + 3 = 18$

191

If there are 33 cherries
to be shared out between 11 children,

there will be 3 cherries for each child.

thirty-three cherries ÷ eleven children =
three cherries each $33 \div 11 = 3$

If there are 33 cherries
to be shared out between 3 children,

each child will get 11 cherries.

thirty-three cherries ÷ three children =
eleven cherries each $33 \div 3 = 11$

REMEMBER:

$33 \div 11 = 3$ $33 \div 3 = 11$ $99 \div 11 = 9$ $99 \div 9 = 11$

192